S0-BAX-619

Open Windows

Fifth Grade Reader

Compiled by Ruth K. Hobbs

 CHRISTIAN LIGHT EDUCATION
A division of Christian Light Publications, Inc.
Harrisonburg, Virginia 22802   (540) 434-0750

OPEN WINDOWS

Christian Light Education, a division of
Christian Light Publications, Inc., Harrisonburg, VA 22802
© 2002 by Christian Light Publications, Inc.
All Rights Reserved.
Printed in Hong Kong

4th Printing, 2010

ISBN: 978-0-87813-948-4

Christian Light Reading to Learn *Series*

Table of Contents

STRONG AND BRAVE

Be Strong

Be strong!
We are not here to play, to dream, to drift;
We have hard work to do, and loads to lift;
Shun not the struggle—face it; 'tis God's gift.

–Maltbie D. Babcock

"Behold, how great a matter a little fire kindleth!"   James 3:5

Enemy in the Wilderness

In many places in the United States today, dialing 911 will have the fire trucks heading for the fire in a matter of minutes. But two hundred years ago 911 was only the number which followed 910. In this story Mercie Stark would have had no idea what a fire department or fire engine or fireman was. Nevertheless, the same purpose and concern behind our modern fire fighting program burned brightly in the hearts of the pioneers.

Old Wullie, the horse, threw up his head and **whinnied.** He didn't like the billowing smoke.

Inside the house, Mercie Stark jumped to her feet. She should have checked on neighbor Zebedee's brush fire a good ten minutes ago. But she had gotten into an argument with Fane. Fane, the son of a fur trader, had cut his foot with an axe and was staying with them while his foot healed.

The breeze that had scarcely stirred the wildflowers in the deer pasture seemed stronger as she hurried toward the sound of the crackling. Bad wind could spread sparks, as Father had warned her. As she came downwind the smoke began to grow **ominously** thick. Even before she saw the flames, she knew this was no false alarm but a real danger. Oh, why had she stopped to argue with Fane!

"Mister Crook!" she shouted. "Mister Zebedee Crook!"

Above the snap of burning brush, above the increasing crackle of flame, she heard no answer. Heedless of the harm his carelessness would cause, Zebedee was likely miles away.

One glance at the flames told Mercie the danger. With pounding heart she began to run up the hill toward Father.

She started screaming even before she saw him. She heard Father's answering shout, and he came rushing down the hill toward her. He had caught the urgency in her voice.

"Zebedee's brush fire has escaped," she panted. Yes, it had escaped like a savage, dangerous, wild creature that had snapped its chain or broken its bars.

"The hoe!" shouted Father as he pounded down toward the smoke.

Mercie ran. The hoe was in the corn patch. Just above the corn patch she had **tethered** Jake, her pet gander. With his injured wing, she knew he couldn't fly to safety. She'd better carry him to a safer place. There was no way to tell yet where the fire would spread or whether she and Father would be able to stop it.

She loosed Jake's tether from the beech trunk, snatched him up under her arm, and grabbed the hoe. It was all she could do to hold down the gander's **flailing** wings and ward off his strong, striking beak. The rolling smoke frightened Jake. Somehow she got him across the stream and tethered him again to a tree where he could calm down in his own good time.

Then breathlessly she rushed back to the fire, coughing now and wiping streaming eyes. The fire had nearly doubled its size from when she had left it moments ago. She spared a worried thought for Fane. But Fane could make his way on his crutch to old Wullie, swing himself up, and ride off to safety. With his bad foot he could not help fight the fire, and he would have the sense to know it.

The heat was too great for them to get within reach and fight the fire itself. But Father swung off to the west horn of the flames a long way ahead of the fire and began clearing a line with his axe.

"Got to burn back," he shouted.

Mercie, right behind him now, flung herself on grass and undergrowth, and began a frantic plucking. She tore out all the small stuff as Father cleared the big. They threw the mass of rubbish toward the side on which the flames approached. With the help of brands that they caught up from the fire, they kindled new flames. They held these new flames back with flailing boughs to keep them from crossing their little cleared path. When the branches dried and caught fire, they flung them into the blaze and tore fresh beaters. Then they watched the flames being sucked in to meet the advancing, bigger flame.

Father was **plying** his axe again, in a new spot. Mercie dropped back to help.

"The brook likely hems in the east end. If we can pinch off twenty, thirty yards at a time, from the west end," he cried, "we can keep hemmin' her in from the west too."

They fought desperately. Just as the fire seemed under

control, it would slip around the end of the line. Time after time a **traitorous** little blaze, kindled by some falling spark on dry leaves, started up right behind them. Then Mercie had to leave Father's side, spring back to beat it out, and race on again to the main line of defense.

A dead sapling came down with a crash. Father attacked another with the same fury. "Scarce a hope we'll save the corn, or even the house. Best we can do is stop the fire from stretching up to forest land and burning everything to the north," he panted between blows.

Eyebrows singed, lips and mouth dry to cracking, Mercie gasped out a horrified "Oh!" She strove still more fiercely with the hated blaze. Her buckskin shirt stung her shoulder. She put up a hand to find a smoldering hole. Quickly she slapped on a handful of earth to extinguish the fire. Sweat poured off her, but mouth, throat, and nose felt parched. No time to desert the defense and go for a drink.

She gave a fleeting thought to Fane. She hoped he was safe, and the rifle too. She hoped he had thought to take Wullie across the stream. If only he would hurry back he might save the kettle, the canister of powder, the bullet mold, and a dozen other things they could not possibly spare or replace. And all, without danger to himself. Perhaps he would think to bring water.

Thorns from berry bushes tore her hands, lashed her face. She still worked on. They had another small fire trace cleared and started a back fire to pinch off another fifty paces of the advancing flame, when Father's axe stopped thudding and he gave a groan. Mercie looked up, horrified. 'Twasn't pain, but something else, had brought out that heart-deep cry.

The wind must have shifted a point or two. It had swung back the flame and circled it around the first trace they had cleared. And now they had all that to do again. Mercie followed Father back to the new line he had started to clear. Grim despair weakened her arms.

It seemed clear that nothing now could save the Stark property. Everything would go. Corn, pumpkins, house, tools, bark stretched out ready for roofing, poles and logs lying this way and that for future building—all would feed the hungry enemy. Why should they keep on fighting when defeat stared them in the face?

Then Mercie realized that Father was fighting for the land of other settlers too. They, like the Starks, had saved year after year. They had put all they had into this new land. You couldn't desert a neighbor or deny him help.

A sudden shout and galloping hoofs! Fane and Wullie thundered up. Hurrying behind, hoes and shovels and axes over their shoulders, came men from the other lots around. Women followed with pails and with quilts to wet in the stream. Men gathered breathlessly in a little group for a moment, making a swift plan. Then they spread out again into a long line. Axes thudded. Spades and hoes scraped the ground clear, far cleaner than Mercie had been able to with her hoe or bare and bleeding hands.

At Father's orders Mercie turned back from the fire line. She joined three or four women to dip water from the stream and carry it forward. They threw bucketfuls of water over the toiling, scorching menfolk. Fane, on Wullie, cantered up and down the line carrying messages. He warned of places where the flames threatened to break through. Fire usually scares horses, but old Wullie did well. He reserved his protests for when an occasional burning leaf dropped scorchingly upon his hide.

The score of menfolk whom Fane had rounded up seemed a pitifully small defense against the roar and crackle of the sweeping flame. But some of this ground was well-trodden trail, and most of it was still damp underbrush. The fire hadn't reached the big trees on the hillside. Eyebrows were singed. One man's beard caught fire and smoldered away close up to its sweat-stained roots. He only laughed and dashed more water on himself. Then he called to Father to ask how much he owed for a close shave.

Then more men arrived from the west, where the fire had been conquered. Gradually the fire seemed to lose heart. The flames didn't roar as high as they had. Smoke still drifted up from the burnt-over ground, but they had conquered the enemy. Together the neighbors had saved their homes.

–Erick Berry

"If any of you lack wisdom, let him ask of God, that giveth to all men liberally, and upbraideth not; and it shall be given him."

James 1:5

Emergency!

Do you know what you should always do first in an emergency? Henry knew, but he faced two responsibilities, and he couldn't do both of them at once.

Henry Bruce stood in the doorway of his cottage home on the northern coast of England. He held his little sister, Lucy, in his arms. His eyes anxiously scanned the road curving around the shore just beyond the house. No sign of Mother yet. The sun dipped below the horizon. Father would soon light the lamp in the lighthouse.

Henry turned to look across the water to the rocky island on which the lighthouse stood. No light gleamed in the lantern. Then Henry's mouth opened in silent **consternation.** A red flag fluttered from the top of the lighthouse. The distress signal! It meant "Come at once!"

"What shall I do?" he whispered in **panic**. That morning Mother had accepted a boat ride across the narrow bay to the village of Braxton to purchase much-needed yarn for winter clothing. She would have to walk the five miles around by the shore coming home. But she had decided that was better than walking both ways.

After coming home for breakfast, Father had gone back to the lighthouse to work. He would spend the night there. That left only Henry to care for Lucy in Mother's absence.

Most lighthouse keepers had assistants who worked **alternate** shifts caring for the light. Mr. Bruce had not asked for an assistant, knowing that sharing the job would result in a **reduction** of his salary. He needed that money to feed and clothe his family, and felt God would help him manage the light alone.

Henry's attention was **riveted** on the distress signal. Then Father's emergency drill training asserted itself. He and Henry had practiced the drill many times.

"The first step," Henry said aloud as he recalled the sequence, "is *'Identify the problem.'*"

Henry's glance darted back to the dark lantern on top of the lighthouse. There fluttered that red distress flag as the wind began to moan and whistle around the rocky island.

"I don't know the problem." Henry answered his own question, fighting down his rising panic.

Then the second step in the emergency drill came to his mind: *"What should I do first?"*

The answer seemed evident. The problem lay at the lighthouse. Father needed help for some reason. Henry must go to the lighthouse. That posed no problem, for he had done that times without number. But what about Lucy? He could not take her along in the rowboat. *If only Mother would come,* he thought in desperation.

"What can I do with you?" Henry demanded as he looked from Lucy to the red flag beckoning him to "Come at once."

"Lucy can go," the toddler said, smiling.

"No, Lucy can't go," Henry declared. "How could I row the boat and handle you? You'd fall overboard a dozen times before we got there."

Then Father's basic rule came to his mind. "If at any point you don't know what to do, ask God to show you."

"Lord, tell me," the boy pleaded. He looked around the small cottage, and spotted Lucy's high chair. "That's it," he cried. "I'll tie you into the chair. Even if you don't like it, you'll be safe till I get back or Mother comes."

So saying, Henry securely strapped the toddler into the high chair. He piled a handful of crackers on the tray and tied a bottle of milk by a cord so Lucy could pull it up if it fell off.

"Now shut your eyes and take a nap like a good girlie," he **admonished** her. Then he lit the lamp and scribbled a note of explanation to his mother. He propped the note where she would see it immediately.

Leaping down over the rocks, he untied the rowboat and soon was pulling for the lighthouse.

The heavy bronze door of the tower opened into a dimly lit room that served as storage place for wood and coal for the lamp. It also held containers of fresh water from the mainland. Henry ran up the stairs to the room used for a kitchen. The next flight of stairs took him to the bedroom. From the bedroom a ladder led to the tower that held the big light.

At every level Henry had called for his father, and his

10

consternation increased as only silence greeted him. Now he entered the dark lantern room and called again. Listening intently, he heard a faint moan on the far side.

"I should have brought a lamp when I first came up," he scolded himself, as he made his way down to the kitchen room and seized the kerosene lamp. At the top of the lighthouse again, the lamp revealed Father lying on the floor. Blood oozed from his left temple.

At first Henry couldn't even think. Panic again seized him. Then he remembered the steps of the emergency drill.

First step: *Identify the problem.* "That's easy. Father's hurt."

Second step: *What should I do first?* "Stop the bleeding," came the answer. Henry successfully did this by binding the wound with one of the clean cloths used in polishing the lantern glass.

All this time Father remained unconscious. "If only Mother were here," Henry whispered desperately to himself. "Surely by now she has read my note." But then he thought, *She has no boat and she can't leave Lucy either.*

Third step: *What do I do next?* To Henry, getting aid for his father obviously was urgent. That meant rowing to the mainland.

Henry brought a pillow from the bedroom and slipped it under his father's head, noting that no blood was seeping through the bandage. He covered him with a blanket. Then he hurried downstairs and outdoors. There he stopped. Rain had begun to fall. So had the darkness. He could see the lights on the mainland, safe and friendly through the gloom. How frighteningly dark it was here on the island.

Suddenly Henry became aware of the reason for the absolute blackness around him. The lamp wasn't lit! He thought of the plaque hanging on the wall in the lighthouse. It was titled "Charge to Keepers" and read, "Light the lamp every evening at sunset and keep it burning bright and clear until sunrise."

As far back as Henry could remember, his father had obeyed that charge. Even when he felt sick he insisted on going to the island and lighting the lamp at sunset. Henry had often heard him say, "By the grace of God no wreck will ever happen on this coast because I failed to keep the light burning." But tonight he had failed to light the lamp at sunset. Even now, there might be a ship headed for the rocks or a boat lost on the water.

In a panic, Henry turned and felt his way back into the lighthouse and raced up into the tower. In a few minutes the lamp flashed out through the rain over the sea. In its brilliant glare, Father stirred and opened his eyes. "The light! The light!" he mumbled.

Henry knelt beside him. "It's lit, Father. Don't worry. What happened? I must fetch the doctor..."

"No, no, don't go. Tend the light." Father closed his eyes and lapsed into unconsciousness again.

Through that long cheerless night Henry kept the lamp burning. A terrible fear never left him. His thoughts alternated between three questions. *Is Father dead? Should I have tried somehow to get to the mainland for help? Did any ships wreck before I lit the lamp?*

Dawn had hardly broken when the exhausted boy heard shouts from the bottom of the lighthouse. Two neighbors came thumping up the stairs. After Henry told his story, they told theirs.

"When we saw that rain coming up, we knew your mother would be caught in it if she walked home around by the shore. So we decided to come home early and bring her along. We lost our bearings because we couldn't see the light. But just as we realized we were hopelessly lost, the light came on and we knew which way to go.

"When your mother read your note she really began to worry and told us to come as soon as we could see to row."

With the coming of full daylight, the neighbors carefully put Father into the boat and took him across the water to the doctor.

Henry never forgot the steps of Father's emergency drill. And all his life he used Father's basic rule: "If at any point you don't know what to do, ask God to help you."

"Take fast hold of instruction; let her not go: keep her; for she is thy life."   Proverbs 4:13

Sleep-Out Below Zero

Find northern Sweden on a globe or map. Run your finger on the same line of latitude over to North America. How would you like to spend a winter night outside in an open sled that close to the North Pole?

Few **foreigners** travel in northern Sweden in the winter because of the extreme cold. As you go north from Stockholm, the capital, the country becomes rougher and wilder, and the climate more severe.

I traveled there in the winter, heading toward Lapland, where you can travel more easily on the frozen swamps and rivers, and the reindeer sled can fly along over the smooth snow. The short days were extremely cold, and if I had not found the people so kind, so cheerful, and so honest, I should have wanted to turn back more than once. But I do not think you can find better people in the world than those who live in the Swedish province of Norrland, **commencing** about two hundred miles north of Stockholm.

A tall, strong race, the Norrlanders have yellow hair and bright blue eyes and the handsomest teeth I ever saw. They

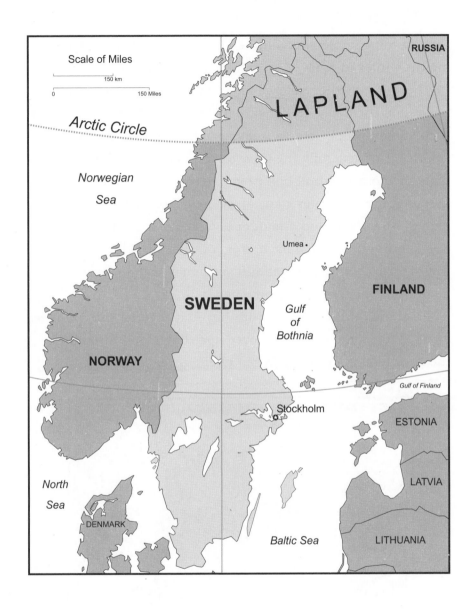

live plainly but comfortably in snug wooden houses, with double windows and doors to keep out the cold. And since they cannot do much outdoor work, they spin and weave and mend their farming implements in the large family room, thus enjoying the winter in spite of its extremely low temperatures.

They have neither railroads nor stages, but the government has established post stations from ten to twenty miles apart. At each station people keep a number of horses, and sometimes vehicles. But generally the traveler has his own sled and simply hires the horses to pull him from one station to another. The keeper of the station or some of the neighboring farmers furnish these horses, and a man or boy goes along with the traveler to bring the animal back. It is a very satisfactory way of traveling, except that sometimes you must wait an hour or more before horses can be obtained.

I had my own sled, filled with hay and covered with reindeer skins to keep me warm. I enjoyed speeding along through the dark forests, over the frozen rivers, or past farms in the

DC Heath and Company

sheltered valleys until long after the stars came out, and the dancing streamers of the **aurora** filled the heavens. I enjoyed getting a warm supper in some dark-red cottage, while the cheerful people sang or told stories around the fire.

The cold increased a little every day, but I became accustomed to it, and soon began to fancy I could endure the Arctic climate better than most foreigners. The temperature fell to zero; then it went down ten degrees below; then twenty, and finally thirty. Dressed in thick furs from head to foot, I did not suffer greatly; but rejoiced when the people assured me that such extreme cold never lasted more than two or three days. Boys of twelve or fourteen often went with me to bring back their fathers' horses, and so long as those lively fellows could face the weather, it would not do for me to act afraid.

One night we viewed a wonderful aurora in the heavens. Streamers of red and blue light darted hither and thither, chasing each other up to the highest part of the sky and down again to the northern horizon. I had never seen a more rapid and brilliant display.

"That means a storm soon," said my postboy; "one always comes after these lights."

Morning dawned gray, and the short day stayed as dark as our twilight. But the temperature had **moderated**, and I traveled onward as fast as possible. Ahead of me stretched a wild and thinly settled area, and I wished to get through it before stopping for the night. Unfortunately, travelers ahead of me had taken the horses at the next station; so I had to wait for another horse to be brought from a neighboring farm. This delayed me so much that at seven o'clock in the evening when

17

snow began to fall, I still had one more station of three Swedish miles before reaching the village where I had intended to spend the night. A Swedish mile equals nearly seven English miles, so this station lay at least twenty miles away.

I took supper while the horse ate his feed. The station keeper had gone on with the earlier travelers to bring his horses back. His wife—a friendly, rosy-faced woman—prepared me some excellent coffee, potatoes, and stewed reindeer meat, upon which I made a satisfactory meal. The house stood on the border of a large, dark forest, and the roar of the icy northern wind in the trees seemed to increase while I waited in the warm room. I did not really want to go on in the wintry storm, but I did want to reach the next village that night.

"A bad night," said the woman, "and my husband will certainly stay at Umea until morning. His name is Neils Petersen, and you will find him at the posthouse when you get there. Lars will take you, and they can come back together."

"Who is Lars?" I asked.

"Our son," said she. "He is getting the horse ready. There is nobody else about the house tonight."

Just then the door opened, and in came Lars. He was about twelve years old and small for his age. I couldn't believe that his mother would let him start on a twenty-mile journey on such a night.

However, I had traveled all over the world in all kinds of weather, in all sorts of vehicles. If this young boy could but show me the way, I would see to our getting there safely.

"Come here, Lars," I said. Then I took him by the hand and asked, "Do you not fear to go so far tonight?"

DC Heath and Company

He looked at me with wondering eyes and smiled, and his mother made haste to say: "You need not fear, sir. Lars is young, but he'll take you safe enough. If the storm doesn't get worse, you'll see Umea by eleven o'clock."

Again I almost decided to stay for I hated to be responsible for the youngster, but Lars changed my mind. He put on his overcoat of sheepskin, tied the lappets of his fur cap under his chin and wound a thick woolen scarf around his neck and across his nose and mouth. I could see nothing but his round blue eyes. Then his mother took down the mittens of hare's fur from the stove, where she had hung them to dry. He put them on, took a short leather whip, and stood ready.

I wrapped myself in my furs, and we went out together. The driving snow cut me in the face like needles, but Lars did not mind it in the least. He jumped into the sled, which he had filled with fresh, soft hay, and tucked in the reindeer skins at the sides. We cuddled together on the narrow seat, making everything close and warm before we set out. I could not see at

19

all after the door of the house had closed until my eyes got used to the darkness. Then the snowy road emerged as a gray strip winding among the dark fir trees. Lars, however, knew the way, and somehow or other we kept the beaten track. He talked to the horse so constantly and so cheerfully that after a while my own spirits began to rise, and the way seemed neither so long nor so disagreeable.

"Ho there, Axel!" he would say. "Keep the road—not too far to the left. Well done! Here's a level stretch; now trot a bit."

So we went on with the runners hissing through the snow for a long time, as it seemed. I began to grow chilly and **shuddered** now and again in my furs. I realized I had been foolish to start out after dark in an open sled when the temperature stood below zero. Even Lars handed me the reins while he swung and beat his arms to keep the blood in **circulation.** He no longer sang little songs and parts of hymns, as when we first set out; but he appeared not in the least alarmed, or even impatient. Whenever I asked (as I did about every five minutes), "Are we nearly there?" he always answered, "A little farther," until grave doubts began spinning in my mind. Did this boy really know where we were? Obviously he did not recognize the increasing seriousness of our situation.

I had decided to tell Lars to turn and go back the way we had come when suddenly the wind seemed to increase.

"Ah," said he, "now I know where we are. One mile more." But one Swedish mile, I remembered, meant seven.

Lars checked the horse and peered anxiously into the darkness. I could see nothing.

"What is the matter?" I finally asked.

"We have got past the hills on the left," he said. "The country is open to the wind, and here the snow drifts worse than anywhere else. If they have not plowed the road tonight, we'll have trouble, even though it has almost stopped snowing."

The law required the farmers to keep the roads plowed open. However, this snow had begun after dark. No need to clear the road till after the storm, or at least till morning.

In only a few minutes the horse sank deep in the snow. He plunged bravely forward, but made little headway, and soon became so exhausted that he stopped. Lars and I arose from the seat and looked around. I saw nothing except some very faint shapes of trees with no sign of an opening through them. In a few minutes the horse started again, and with great effort carried us a few yards farther.

"Shall we get out and try to find the road?" said I. At that point my confidence in being able to handle the situation drifted away like my frozen breath into the night.

"That would not help," Lars answered. "In these new drifts we will sink to the waist. Wait a little, and we shall get through this one."

It was as he said. Another pull brought us through the deep part of the drift, and we reached a place where the snow seemed quite shallow. But it was not the hard, smooth surface of the road, but uneven ground covered with roots and bushes. Bidding Axel stand still, Lars jumped out of the sled and began wading around among the trees. Then I got out on the other side, but had not proceeded ten steps before I began to sink so deeply into the loose snow that I gladly returned to the sled. I felt desperate and wondered how we should ever get out of it.

Nothing I had ever experienced prepared me for coping with what had suddenly become a life-threatening emergency.

I shouted to Lars, in order to guide him, and before long he also floundered back to the sled.

"If I could find the road," said he, "I could get onto it again. But I can't find it so I think we must stay here all night."

"We shall freeze to death in an hour!" I cried. I was already chilled to the bone and my feet had turned numb. The wind had made me very drowsy, and I knew that if I slept I should soon freeze. In a panic, I began to flail my arms and stamp my feet to restore the circulation.

"No, we won't freeze!" remarked Lars, cheerfully. "I am a Norrlander, and Norrlanders don't freeze. I went with the men to hunt bear last winter, and we spent several nights in the snow. Besides, I know what my father did with a gentleman from Stockholm on this very road, and we'll do it tonight."

"What did they do?" I asked eagerly, ready to follow instructions, but greatly wondering how he would implement a sleep-out below zero.

"Let me take care of Axel first," said Lars. "We can spare him some hay and one reindeer skin."

It was a slow and difficult task to unharness the horse, but we accomplished it at last. Lars then led him under the drooping branches of a fir tree and tied him to one of them. He gave him an armful of hay, and fastened the reindeer skin upon his back. Axel began to eat, perfectly satisfied with the arrangement.

I could hardly endure the calmness with which Lars spread the remaining hay evenly over the bottom of the sled and covered it with the skins, which he tucked in very firmly on the side towards the wind. Why didn't he hurry? Why didn't he tell me what I must do? I felt myself freezing stiff on my feet as I watched him moving around in the dim light.

Finally he lifted the skins on the other side and said, "Now take off your fur coat. Quick! Lay it over the hay, and then creep under it."

DC Heath and Company

I obeyed as rapidly as possible. For an instant I shuddered in the icy air, but the next moment I lay stretched in the bottom of the sled, sheltered from the wind. I held up the ends of the reindeer skins while Lars took off his coat and crept in beside me. Then we drew the skins down and pressed the hay against them. When the wind seemed entirely shut out, Lars said we must pull off our boots, untie our scarfs, and so loosen our clothes that they would not feel tight upon any part of the body. Loosening even one piece of clothing did not make sense to me, but Lars explained that doing so created air spaces to trap our body heat. So again I obeyed, realizing finally that my life depended on following Lars' instructions.

After we did this and lay close together, warming each other, I found that the chill gradually passed out of my blood. My hands and feet no longer felt numb; a delightful feeling of comfort crept over me, and I lay as snugly as in the best bed. I did not feel the lack of fresh air, for enough air came in under the skins to prevent us from feeling oppressed.

There was barely space for the two of us to lie, with no room to turn over or roll about. But in five minutes, I think, we fell sound asleep, and I dreamed of gathering peaches on a warm August day at home. In fact, I did not wake up thoroughly during the night; neither did Lars, though it seemed to me that we both talked in our sleep. But as I must have talked English and he Swedish, there could have been no connection between our remarks. I remember that his warm, soft hair pressed against my chin, and that his feet reached no farther than my knees.

Just as I was beginning to feel a little cramped and stiff

from lying so still, a cold wind on my face aroused me. Lars had risen up on his elbow and peeped out from under the skins.

"I think it must be near six o'clock," he said. "The sky is clear, and I see the big star. We can start in another hour."

I felt so much refreshed that I wanted to set out immediately; but Lars remarked, very sensibly, that we still could not find the road.

Then Axel whinnied.

"Here come the farmers clearing the road," cried Lars, and immediately began to put on his boots, his scarf, and heavy coat. I did the same, and in no time we heard shouts and the crack of whips. We harnessed Axel to the sled and proceeded slowly in the direction of the sounds, which came, as we presently saw, from a company of farmers, out plowing the road.

They had six pairs of horses hitched to a wooden frame something like the bow of a ship, pointed in front and spreading out to a breadth of ten or twelve feet. The device not only cut through the drifts but packed the snow, leaving a good, solid road behind it. After it had passed, we sped along merrily in the cold morning twilight. In little more than an hour we reached the posthouse at Umea, where we found Lars' father preparing to return home. He waited, nevertheless, until we had eaten a good warm breakfast. Then I said good-bye to both and went on towards Lapland.

Some weeks afterward, on my return to Stockholm, I stopped at the same little station. This time the weather had moderated, and the father would have gone with me to the next posthouse; but I preferred to take my little bedfellow and sled-fellow. We had a merry trip of two or three hours, and then I took leave of Lars forever. In later years, I smiled when I remembered how I, a grown man, had so eagerly followed the instructions of a young boy. And I still shudder each time I recall that bitter night when Lars and I slept out below zero.

—Bayard Taylor

Cold Winter

Cold winter now is in the wood,
The moon wades deep in snow.
Pile balsam boughs about the sills,
And let the fires glow!

The cows must stand in the dark barn,   5
The horses stamp all day.
Now shall the housewife bake her pies
And keep her kitchen gay.

The cat sleeps warm beneath the stove,
The dog on paws outspread;   10
But the brown deer with flinching hide
Seeks for a sheltered bed.

The fox steps hungry through the brush,
The lean hawk coasts the sky.
"Winter is in the wood!" the winds   15
In the warm chimney cry.

– Elizabeth Coatsworth

Chinook[1]

For five long months the snow had lain
Hollowed and heaped on the frozen plain,
Choking gullies and rising high
Out of buried bluffs to the leaden sky.

Monster drifts stretched grey-white arms   5
Around the buildings on prairie farms
And only the poles of the telephone line
Broke the waste with their thin design.

Then, silent and swift in the night it came,
That warm west wind with the magic name . . .   10
Snow fled the hills and the hilltops browned,
Fallow and pasture showed virgin ground.

Drifts dissolved, and their rivulets grew
From trickle, to stream, into glistening slough,
Where aspen and willow marched down to drink 15
Fresh new life from the icy brink.

---

[1]chinook – shi nŭk′

Silent and swift on the warm wind's crest
Spring blew in to the welcoming West;
On a new brown hill I lingered to look
And whispered the magic name, "Chinook." 20

–Eleanor Chance Long

"Charity . . . beareth all things, believeth all things,
hopeth all things, endureth all things."   1 Corinthians 13:7

Till I Have Proof

On the northwest coast of France live the sturdy fisher
folk of Brittany. They love the sea, for it is the means by
which they live. They fear it too, for it sometimes brings
them great sorrow.

Michel[1] trudged home to supper. All day he had forked
heavy, slippery seaweed into carts. His arms and legs ached,
but he had earned five francs. That would be something to tell
his Uncle Ives[2] when he got back from his voyage to the Bay of
Biscay.

The seaweed, washed up on the beach by a month's storm,
was community property, prized as fertilizer and as bedding
for the livestock. The mayor had appointed a day for each family to gather its share, and an absent citizen had hired Michel
to harvest his part of the sea crop.

As the boy started home, the world began to darken;
and looking at the sky, Michel saw a great mounting cloud
obscuring the blue. As he opened the cottage door, a sudden

---

[1]Michel – mē shel′

[2]Ives – ē vā′

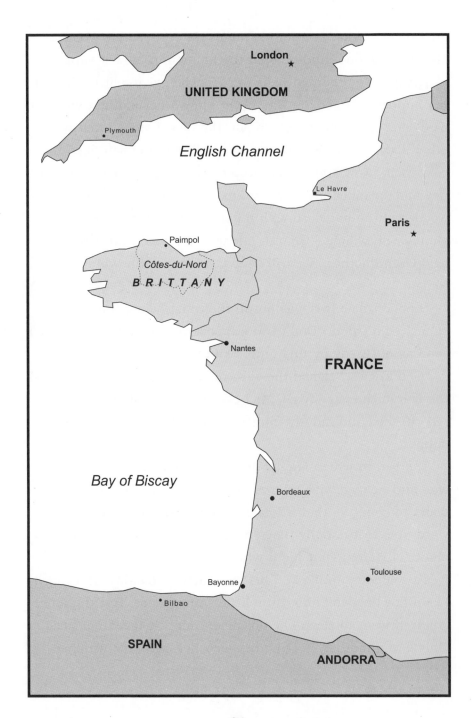

gust nearly jerked it from his hand. He dropped his wooden shoes at the door and entered the kitchen in his felt slippers.

His grandmother sat near the fireplace, giving little Martha her supper. The toddler had never known her mother, who had died soon after she was born. On the hearthstone knelt his other sister Guen. An appetizing smell of frying fish filled the cozy room. Now and then a drop of rain came down the chimney and splashed into the pan, making a great sizzling. The wooden shutters closed with a bang, shutting out the last glimmer of twilight. "Go out, Michel, and fasten them open," said Grandmother; "we will keep the lamp in the window tonight."

"I hope Uncle Ives was far off the coast before this storm came," said Guen. "Don't you suppose the *Jeanot*[3] has reached the Bay of Biscay by this time, Grandmother?"

"God knows," sighed the old woman. She got up and turned the fish in the pan. Josef, Michel's younger brother, came in red-cheeked and muddy from a game of ball, and they ate supper.

The bed in which Michel and Josef slept was built into the wall and heaped with pillows and bedding. It had sliding doors to close, so that it looked like a handsome carved wardrobe. But usually they stood open, showing the pretty chintz curtains. That night when Michel, sitting on Uncle Ives's sea chest, pulled off his stockings, the storm still raged like a howling wolf about the little stone house. But the four children went to sleep like dormice under their feather beds. Only Grandmother, peering between her curtains, watched

---

[3]Jeanot – zhä nō′

32

American Book Company

the flickering lamp all night long.

Michel Karadoc had never gone beyond the smell of the sea, and there was **brine** in his blood. He knew that he, too, sooner or later, like his father and all his forebears, would become a fisherman. In fact, he lived for the day when, as cabin boy, he would take ship under Uncle Ives for Iceland and the Arctic Circle; for Michel lived in the town of Paimpol, in that part of Brittany called the *Côtes-du-Nord.*

From this port every year in March a fishing fleet sails on the **ebbing** tide for northern waters. They return in August for a few weeks' **respite** before starting another voyage to the Bay of

Biscay to buy salt for the next year's catch. Toward September those who have not slipped forever into the silence of the North come back to their homes for the cozy winter months, there to make ready for a fresh voyage in the spring. But there are always some for whom there is only a tablet in the gray church by the sea, like the one for Michel's father: "Jules Karadoc, lost on the Iceland Coast." And under the darkened rafters hang models of many a brave little ship gone down.

For the people of Brittany, storm and shipwreck are the things of every day. They work and eat and sleep as usual; but the women, who do not go to sea, sigh with the wind and pray as they work. They have no respite from fear and worry.

The next morning, after Josef and Guen had gone to school, Michel, taking a pail, ran down to the beach for clams. The sun shone again, the tide ebbed, and only new banks of sea-weed and driftwood flung high on the beach gave any sign of last night's storm.

Michel dug busily for clams, detecting their presence with the keenness of experience, and then with a full pail started homeward. As he skirted the town, the clack of many wooden shoes hurrying over the **cobbles** caught his ear. He saw people running through the streets. Full of curiosity, Michel ran head-long for the square in the center of the town.

About the telegraph office pressed a silent group of women, the tragedy of the sea written on their faces. No one spoke. Only the rapid click of the telegraph key came through the open door. Then a man appeared holding high a slip of paper.

"Susanne Allanic," he called; and added quickly, "Your man's safe!"

Susanne, standing on the edge of the crowd with a baby in her arms, threw up her head, gave a cry, and broke into sobs.

"What's the matter?" asked Michel sharply, for Susanne's husband was one of the *Jeanot*'s crew.

"The *Jeanot*'s gone down," said a woman breathlessly. "Four men are missing. We don't know who they are."

Michel stood stunned. The sunlight seemed suddenly wiped from the world. "The *Jeanot*'s gone down! The *Jeanot*'s gone down!" kept pounding through his brain.

He knew he would have to tell his grandmother in just those words; he could think of no others. There was no obscuring the truth from her. He turned toward home. At the gate he met a white-faced grandmother, and he knew that she had heard.

"The *Jeanot*'s—" he stammered trembling.

"Yes," said Grandmother, "but Ives will telegraph." And she took the pail of clams from him and went into the house to make the chowder.

American Book Company

They all knew now that they had gotten the spent end of a great tempest, which had swept the coast from Spain north-ward, and that the *Jeanot,* struggling to keep to the open sea, had crashed on the rocks below the Bay of Biscay.

From obscure Spanish towns belated telegrams kept coming in all that week. Three bodies had been washed ashore, and eleven men were accounted for. No word came about Ives Karadoc.

Some sailors had come home with the story of the wreck. After the break-up of the *Jeanot,* they had seen Ives clinging to a floating barrel. This was the last known of him. So the days dragged on, hollow and dark.

People went back to their daily affairs, and began to talk of other things than the wreck of the *Jeanot.* But in Michel's home things had changed. Laughter had died away from the hearthstone. A knock or a strange step on the cobbles set their hearts beating, and every night the little lamp burned in the window.

"A ship has picked up Ives and taken him to some far coun-try," persisted Grandmother. "We shall hear, we shall hear." But one morning Michel found her all in a heap near the fire-place, weeping with her apron over her head. That night she did not put the lamp in the window.

He himself would not give up, and with hot protest in his heart he started for the headland beyond the village where one could look far out at sea. At that point they had gathered to watch for the Iceland fleet when it had cruised home less than a month ago. Then the *Jeanot* had led the others, her sails agleam in the setting sun. And now the *Jeanot* had gone down!

Why, she was as familiar and friendly and dear as the kitchen itself! And Uncle Ives was such a jolly young uncle, so full of understanding! And the children had all adored him! He couldn't be gone forever! "I won't believe it till I have proof," Michael declared out loud as he walked along.

Michel pushed his way through the gorse that pricked thickly about him. At the summit of the headland stood a great stone cross, its carvings worn by centuries of wind and brine. Here women who had waited long for men at sea came to pray. On the step, with his cap pressed to his breast, Michel knelt. His heart was too full to pray in words. Besides, what could he say since God already knew how much he wanted Uncle Ives back? "I won't give up hope," he whispered with brave determination, "till I have proof."

After a while Michel stood up, and shading his eyes, gazed seaward. There where the straits led into the open channel lay a small island, and round its point came the Paimpol fishing fleet, returning for the night. As they drew nearer, Michel could distinguish each boat by some well-known mark. The high curved prow identified Raoul's boat, a black and green

American Book Company

trawler. He saw the orange patch on Jean Baptist's gray sail. But among the well-known boats he spotted a stranger with tawny sails and a bulky hull larger than the rest. What boat was that? Pricked by curiosity, Michel forgot his grief. Slipping and crashing down the hillside, he raced back by way of the beach, hoping to reach the wharf almost as soon as the boats did.

When he reached the village, the boats had already moored. A crowd had gathered, and Michel could see the sailors carrying someone on a stretcher from the strange boat.

A cheer went up from the crowd. Michel, dodging under elbows, squirmed his way nimbly to the inner circle. He could see a form wrapped in blankets on the stretcher around which the men pressed eagerly.

"Is it a rescue?" he asked, for such things often happened.

"Hello, old pal!" cried a familiar voice, and Michel stood speechless. The darkness suddenly fell from him, and the world became real again, with all his broken courage coming back.

"Uncle Ives!" he cried, his voice high with excitement. "I didn't believe you were dead." And then all at once he knew how terribly afraid he had been. "But Grandmother did," he continued. His chin quivered, and great tears fell on the wharf.

"Look here, Michel," said Uncle Ives softly, "you cut ahead and tell her there's nothing the matter with me but a broken leg."

And so Michel flew home, the swift forerunner of the triumphant procession that wound from the landing to the Karadoc cottage.

No one heard a word of Uncle Ives's story that night. Grandmother sent them all to bed earlier than usual and closed the door on eager neighbors. But the next day in the sunny garden, where bees bobbed in and out of the honeysuckle, they heard of the dark night when the *Jeanot* went down in a crash of wind and foam. They heard of the miracle by which Uncle Ives, clinging to an empty salt keg, had been drawn away from the rocks by the ebbing tide. They heard how a fishing boat had picked him up the next day, unconscious and with one leg broken from a blow of which he knew nothing. The fishing boat, bound for the French coast, had taken him along and put him in the hospital. After he was on the mend, they had gone out of their way on their next cruise to bring the wounded man home.

Michel and Josef carved a model of the *Jeanot* and rigged it. They took it to the little gray church by the sea, where it hangs in the dim shadows of the roof, a reminder of the safe return of Uncle Ives.

—Anna Milo Upjohn

Down on the Shore

Down on the shore, on the sunny shore
  Where the salt smell cheers the land;
Where the tide moves bright under boundless light,
  And the surge on the glittering strand;
Where the children wade in the glittering pools,   5
  Or run from the froth in play;
Where the swift little boats with milk-white wings
  Are crossing the sapphire bay,
And the ship in full sail, with a fortunate gale,
  Holds proudly on her way;   10
Where the nets are spread on the grass to dry,
And asleep, hard by, the fishermen lie,
Under the tent of the warm blue sky,
With the hushing wave on the golden floor
  To sing their lullaby.   15

Down on the shore, on the stormy shore!
   Beset by a growling sea,
Whose mad waves leap on the rocky steep,
   Like wolves up a traveler's tree.
Where the foam flies wide, and an angry blast   20
   Blows the curlew off, with a screech;
Where the brown sea wrack[1], torn up by the roots,
   Is flung out of fishes' reach;
Where the tall ship rolls on the hidden shoals,
   And scatters her planks on the beach;   25
Where slate and straw through the village spin.
And a cottage fronts the fiercest din,
With a sailor's wife sitting sad within,
Hearkening the wind and the water's roar,
   Till at last her tears begin.   30

–Author Unknown

---

[1]sea wrack – sea weed

"A friend loveth at all times, and a brother is born for adversity."

Proverbs 17:17

Brothers in Danger

How would you like to go adventuring in the jungle with two African boys? Simba and his friend would show you elephants and lions—not lazy, tame ones across the moat of a zoo, but real, wild ones. You would see another dangerous animal too. But unless you can run fast and climb a tree in a wink, you'd be safer just reading about what happened to Simba.

Simba and Kimani lay hidden behind a bush on the African hillside. They were laughing at the antics of four little elephant calves below them. The youngsters, squealing with glee, chased each other in and out of the thick jungle growth, bumping more and more frequently into the legs of their giant elders.

Suddenly a cow, her patience exhausted, raised her trunk and smacked her calf soundly. He gave a bawl of pain and ran under her to escape further punishment, while his three companions went a safe distance away. From there they watched their own mothers with **shrewd** eyes.

The scene so **entranced** the boys that they inched a little closer in order to get a better view of the young elephants. As they did so, Simba's hand tightened suddenly on his friend's arm. One of the great beasts had turned and was looking toward the spot where the boys lay hidden.

She spread her vast, fanlike ears and raised her trunk. The tip of it waved gently from side to side as she searched the air for more of the scent that had alarmed her. With a slow and frightening intentness she stared directly toward the bush behind which the boys crouched.

Simba and Kimani did not wait to see what she would do. Wriggling through the grass on their stomachs, they slid over the top of the hill like two brown eels and then, taking to their heels, ran with all their might.

On the top of another hill, about a quarter of a mile away, they paused and looked back. They could see the huge elephant outlined against the sky. She stood where they had crouched five minutes before. The bugle of her voice shrilled at them across the valley as they watched her from a safe distance.

The two boys walked on, searching for more adventure. Already that morning they had wandered far from their village. After they had walked another mile or so, they saw a group of lions resting in the shade of a tree. Simba and Kimani made a very respectful detour around the great tawny creatures.

The beasts watched the two boys sleepily, all except one lioness who rose **lithely** to her feet and stared at them intently. Her tail switched from side to side.

Simba and Kimani instantly checked the presence of nearby trees in case she decided to come nearer. But she evidently considered them harmless, for she finally turned and lay

43

down, stretching out lazily like a great house cat.

They startled a flock of guinea fowl, which rose on thundering wings. A swift arrow from Simba's bow brought a fat hen tumbling to earth. While Kimani plucked and cleaned her, Simba started a fire with a stick and a stone. Soon the boys were eating the hot, tender flesh of the fowl, and in a short time had picked her bones clean.

When they had finished, Kimani said, "Look at our shadows, Simba. We must turn back toward the village, or night will catch us outside the walls."

"True," replied Simba, "we must soon return. But first let us go down to the river. We shall have plenty of time, for we **loitered** as we came, and going back we can hurry."

Halfway down the hill, the **vague** sound of voices made them stop suddenly. Both crouched, their slim bodies seeming to become part of the brown bushes about them.

"Strange men," whispered Simba shrewdly. "Enemies, perhaps. Let us steal close and look at them."

Proceeding slowly through the undergrowth, the boys wormed their way toward the sound and shortly found themselves crouching among the giant ferns at the edge of the flowing stream. Their eyes widened with wonder and excitement at what they saw on the other side.

Across the stream, in the shade of a spreading tree, stood several tents. They saw some dark-skinned natives like themselves going in and out. But what held the wide-eyed attention of Simba and Kimani were the people who sat in low chairs before one of the tents.

"White people!" whispered Simba.

On only one other occasion had the boys seen a white man. Years ago, one had come to their village. But here were more of the strange creatures right before their eyes. The woman spoke in a soft and gentle voice, and they could see golden hair straying from under the brim of her white helmet.

"Her hair," whispered Simba in entranced wonder, "Like the edge of a cloud at sunset."

The white woman raised her voice and called. The next instant a white boy came out of the tent and walked over to her, putting his arm across her shoulders. She spoke to him in words the watchers could not understand.

Simba and Kimani gazed spellbound. A boy about their age, with fair skin and hair, and blue eyes!

The native boys studied every detail of his clothing, from the brown helmet on his head to the sturdy shoes on his feet. When he took a shiny thing from his pocket and put it to his lips, the crouching boys were not prepared for the ear-splitting screech of the whistle. The sudden, piercing sound startled them so that they nearly rolled into the stream.

Simba and Kimani found the wonders across the stream so interesting that they thought nothing of time. But at last they tore themselves away and stole back through the jungle to the edge of the plains. A glance at the sun told them that darkness would fall in less than two hours, and before them lay ten miles of wild and savage land. They broke into long, swift strides, and just as the short dusk ended, they raced through the entrance to the village.

"What we have seen this day shall remain a secret between us," said Simba as they parted for the night. "Tomorrow we will go again and watch these strange white people."

"Yes, and let us start early," replied Kimani.

But Kimani did not go the next day as they had planned. His older brother, who had been herding the family cattle, fell ill, and it became Kimani's duty to sit on the hillside and watch the cows. Simba, however, had no such responsibility. So early that morning he trotted briskly out of the village gate on his way to the white people's camp.

Several hours later Simba crouched in his hiding-place among the giant ferns by the river bank, watching every move of the white boy. He learned his name, *Jack,* and said it over and over to himself.

Through the long days that followed, the entranced brown boy lay in the jungle shadows, watching the white boy. Sometimes Jack would go out hunting with his father, and on such occasions Simba did not dare to follow for fear the keen-eyed gun-bearers who went with them would discover him.

And every evening he reported to Kimani what he had seen. His explanations often were vague, for many times he did not understand what the white people were doing.

Seven days passed in this fashion, Simba tirelessly studying the strange people across the river. Then on the eighth morning he had the greatest adventure of his life. The two white men had gone away with the gun-bearers, leaving Jack alone with his mother. The boy sat cleaning his small rifle. That job finished, he arose and began walking restlessly about the camp. Finally he disappeared into the jungle.

Instantly Simba rose from his hiding-place and lithely slipped through the thickets directly across the river from

Jack. Then like a brown shadow he kept pace with the white boy, who strode noisily along on the opposite bank.

Suddenly Simba stood still, scarcely breathing. Jack had turned toward the stream and crossed in the shallows! A minute later he came up the bank on the same side of the river as Simba. A vague anxiety seized Simba. This white boy had no business coming here alone with no weapon of any kind. Simba followed noiselessly.

All at once Jack turned abruptly and struck out toward the open country beyond the jungle. Simba turned in the same direction. In a short time both boys had reached the edge of the forest, though they were some distance apart. As the white boy left the shadows, Simba peered out cautiously. And then his breath hissed inward in startled terror at what he saw.

Jack was strolling slowly toward a huge rock in an open, grassy spot, but he could not see the wild buffalo that grazed on the opposite side. From time to time, Simba saw the animal raise his immense head and sniff the wind in a vague disturbed way.

Simba knew that buffalo in a herd usually took off instantly at sight or scent of a foe. But he also knew that under similar circumstances a single buffalo would undoubtedly charge.

The instant Jack walked around the rock, the buffalo would discover him. Then, before the boy could make a single move toward climbing to safety, the beast would thunder down on him in a savage, deadly charge.

Simba realized that he would have to do whatever could be done to save the life of the unsuspecting boy walking so innocently toward certain death. He must attract the brute's attention to himself before Jack stepped from behind the rock.

Simba looked back into the jungle. He couldn't climb those big trees. A rapid survey of the ropy vines hanging nearby convinced him they would not serve his purpose, either. He could go up them like a monkey, but the charging buffalo would break them like strings, and he would crash to earth, where the beast would trample him to death.

Now his darting eye focused on a tall tree that grew slightly out in the open at his left. One branch, well above the ground, grew straight out from the trunk. Could he reach it? It would be close—deadly close—but it was the only way.

Simba stepped into the open and shouted. Jack spied him and stood gaping in astonishment.

The buffalo lifted his massive head, thrusting forward his wet black muzzle to scent this sudden enemy. Instantly Simba raised his bow, and let fly an arrow. Then he dropped his weapon and ran.

As the arrow pierced the buffalo's tough hide, he gave a deep bellow and went into lightning action. Simba heard the thunder of the buffalo's hoofs, and from the corner of his eye saw the animal sweeping toward him at terrible speed.

Nearer the tree—a few more flying strides—and Simba leaped. His clutching fingers caught the branch, and as his body left the ground the buffalo passed beneath him.

Jack, instantly aware of the danger, had begun to scramble up the side of the boulder. His heavy shoes made the climb a hard one, but fear drove him on, and in a short time he perched on the top of the rock, pale and gasping, looking across at the brown stranger in the tree. The buffalo, bellowing deeply, paced back and forth between the two.

Now that the moment of danger had passed, Jack wanted to thank Simba for saving his life. He raised his arm and waved. Simba waved back.

"I guess I would have been deader than a doornail if it hadn't been for you," shouted Jack. "Say, you're the fastest runner I ever saw," he added in admiration.

Simba shook with excitement. The strange white boy was actually talking to him. So in his own language Simba shouted back, "It didn't take you long to get on that rock, white boy." Though neither one of them understood a word the other said, the two talked back and forth.

The angry rumblings of the buffalo convinced them that the beast had made up his mind to camp there. Simba knew he and the white boy might have to spend the night right where they were. Jack's parents would have no idea where to begin searching for him.

But suddenly the boy on the rock stood up. He pulled that shiny thing from his pocket and put it to his lips. Again Simba was startled by the ear-splitting screech, louder than any jungle bird he had ever heard. Evidently Jack had been missed, for almost immediately there came a distant answering shout.

Five minutes more, then suddenly with a startling roar that nearly dislodged the youngsters from their perches, the crack of a heavy rifle sounded from the edge of the jungle. The gray-black mass of the buffalo tottered and fell. Then Jack's father and mother and several natives burst from the concealment of the forest.

During the time between the death of the buffalo and the

arrival of these people who all talked at once, Jack had jumped down from the rock and Simba had dropped from the tree. Jack's feet had hardly touched the ground when he was in his mother's arms.

Simba shrank back, suddenly shy. He tried to slip away, but Jack grasped him by the hand and led him into the circle where the white people stood.

"Here he is, Mother!" he cried. "Here's the boy who saved my life. I never saw anyone run so fast." And Jack told the whole story to an entranced audience.

Simba could not understand Jack's excited words, but he knew the meaning of the smiles of thankful admiration on everyone's faces. The warm handclasp of Jack's father and the tears in the blue eyes of his mother made Simba think of a proverb in his tribe, "Great danger makes all men brothers." The boy's heart swelled with joy.

What a tale he would have to tell Kimani and the rest of his village that night!

—Alden G. Stevens

"There is no restraint to the LORD to save by many or by few."

1 Samuel 14:6

The Army That Was Too Big

Because Israel had forsaken God and turned to idols, the Lord allowed the Midianites to invade their land. The Israelites fled from their homes to dens and caves in the mountains while the Midianites took over their country, destroying the crops and animals.

Of course, the idols Israel worshiped could not help them, so they finally cried unto the Lord. God, in His everlasting love and mercy, heard them and came to their rescue. This account from the Book of Judges tells how He did it.

[6:12] And the angel of the LORD appeared unto him [Gideon], and said unto him, The LORD is with thee, thou mighty man of valour.

[13] And Gideon said unto him, Oh my Lord, if the LORD be with us, why then is all this **befallen** us? and where be all his miracles which our fathers told us of, saying, Did not the LORD bring us up from Egypt? but now the LORD hath forsaken us, and delivered us into the hands of the Midianites.[1]

[14] And the LORD looked upon him, and said, Go in this thy might, and thou shalt save Israel from the hand of the

---

[1]Midianites – mid′ ē ǝn īts

Midianites: have not I sent thee?

¹⁵ And he said unto him, Oh my Lord, wherewith shall I save Israel? behold, my family is poor in Manasseh,² and I am the least in my father's house.

¹⁶ And the LORD said unto him, Surely I will be with thee, and thou shalt **smite** the Midianites as one man.

³³ Then all the Midianites and the Amalekites³ and the children of the east were gathered together, and went over, and pitched in the valley of Jezreel. ³⁴ But the Spirit of the LORD came upon Gideon, and he blew a trumpet; and Abiezer⁴ was gathered after him. ³⁵ And he sent messengers throughout all Manasseh; who also was gathered after him: and he sent messengers unto Asher, and unto Zebulun,⁵ and unto Naphtali;⁶ and they came up to meet them.

³⁶ And Gideon said unto God, If thou wilt save Israel by mine hand, as thou hast said, ³⁷ Behold, I will put a **fleece** of wool in the floor; and if the dew be on the fleece only, and it be dry upon all the earth beside, then shall I know that thou wilt save Israel by mine hand, as thou hast said.

³⁸ And it was so: for he rose up early on the morrow, and thrust the fleece together, and wringed the dew out of the fleece, a bowl full of water.

³⁹ And Gideon said unto God, Let not thine anger be hot against me, and I will speak but this once: let me prove, I pray thee, but this once with the fleece; let it now be dry only upon the fleece, and upon all the ground let there be dew. ⁴⁰ And

---

²Manasseh – mə nas′ ə

³Amalekites – a mal′ ək īts

⁴Abiezer – ā bī ē′ zər

⁵Zebulun – zeb′ yə lən

⁶Naphtali – naf′ tə lī

God did so that night: for it was dry upon the fleece only, and there was dew on all the ground.

⁷:¹ Then Jerubbaal,⁷ who is Gideon, and all the people that were with him, rose up early, and pitched beside the well of Harod: so that the host of the Midianites were on the north side of them, by the hill of Moreh, in the valley.

² And the LORD said unto Gideon, The people that are with thee are too many for me to give the Midianites into their hands, lest Israel **vaunt** themselves against me, saying, Mine own hand hath saved me. ³ Now therefore go to, proclaim in the ears of the people, saying, Whosoever is fearful and afraid, let him return and depart early from mount Gilead. And there returned of the people twenty and two thousand; and there remained ten thousand.

⁴ And the LORD said unto Gideon, The people are yet too many; bring them down unto the water, and I will try them for thee there: and it shall be, that of whom I say unto thee, This shall go with thee, the same shall go with thee; and of whomsoever I say unto thee, This shall not go with thee, the same shall not go. ⁵ So he brought down the people unto the water: and the LORD said unto Gideon, Every one that lappeth of the water with his tongue, as a dog lappeth, him shalt thou set by himself; likewise every one that boweth down upon his knees to drink.

⁶ And the number of them that lapped, putting their hand to their mouth, were three hundred men: but all the rest of the people bowed down upon their knees to drink water. ⁷ And the LORD said unto Gideon, By the three hundred men that lapped

---

⁷Jerubbaal – jer ə bā′ əl

will I save you, and deliver the Midianites into thine hand: and let all the other people go every man unto his place.

8 So the people took **victuals** in their hand, and their trumpets: and he sent all the rest of Israel every man unto his tent, and retained those three hundred men: and the host of Midian was beneath him in the valley.

9 And it came to pass the same night, that the LORD said unto him, Arise, get thee down unto the host; for I have delivered it into thine hand. 10 But if thou fear to go down, go thou with Phurah[8] thy servant down to the host:

11 And thou shalt hear what they say; and afterward shall thine hands be strengthened to go down unto the host. Then went he down with Phurah his servant unto the outside of the armed men that were in the host.

12 And the Midianites and the Amalekites and all the children of the east lay along in the valley like grasshoppers for multitude; and their camels were without number, as the sand by the sea side for multitude. 13 And when Gideon was come, behold, there was a man that told a dream unto his fellow, and said, Behold, I dreamed a dream, and, lo, a cake of barley bread tumbled into the host of Midian, and came unto a tent, and smote it that it fell, and overturned it, that the tent lay along. 14 And his fellow answered and said, This is nothing else save the sword of Gideon the son of Joash, a man of Israel: for into his hand hath God delivered Midian, and all the host.

15 And it was so, when Gideon heard the telling of the dream, and the **interpretation** thereof, that he worshipped, and returned into the host of Israel, and said, Arise; for the

---

8Phurah – fyür′ ə

LORD hath delivered into your hand the host of Midian.

¹⁶ And he divided the three hundred men into three companies, and he put a trumpet in every man's hand, with empty pitchers, and lamps within the pitchers. ¹⁷ And he said unto them, Look on me, and do likewise: and, behold, when I come to the outside of the camp, it shall be that, as I do, so shall ye do. ¹⁸ When I blow with a trumpet, I and all that are with me, then blow ye the trumpets also on every side of all the camp, and say, The sword of the LORD, and of Gideon.

¹⁹ So Gideon, and the hundred men that were with him, came unto the outside of the camp in the beginning of the middle watch; and they had but newly set the watch: and they blew the trumpets, and brake the pitchers that were in their hands. ²⁰ And the three companies blew the trumpets, and brake the pitchers, and held the lamps in their left hands, and the trumpets in their right hands to blow withal: and they cried, The sword of the LORD, and of Gideon. ²¹ And they stood every man in his place round about the camp: and all the host ran, and cried, and fled.

Judges 6:12-16; 6:33—7:21

*When Gideon's men got their drinks, do you suppose
any of them saw what the author of this poem saw when
she took a drink?*

The Spring

A little mountain spring I found
That fell into a pool;
I made my hands into a cup
And caught the sparkling water up—
It tasted fresh and cool.   5

A solemn little frog I spied
Upon the rocky brim;
He looked so boldly in my face,
I'm certain that he thought the place
Belonged by rights to him.   10

—Rose Fyleman

It Happened Long Ago

I Remember, I Remember

I remember, I remember,
    The house where I was born
The little window, where the sun
    Came peeping in at morn.

I remember, I remember,
    The roses, red and white,
The violets and the lily-cups,
    Those flowers made of light!

– Thomas Hood

"Prove all things; hold fast that which is good."

To Prove a Proverb

Deep down in his heart, David knew Mother's latest proverb couldn't be true. And he had the perfect chance to prove it.

"David, I'm leaving a job for you." Mother took her pocketbook from the drawer and glanced out the window to see if Father had brought the carriage to the door.

"Listen, dear. I want you to get to filling the water barrel so that we'll have plenty of water tonight and tomorrow."

"Aw, Mother. Must I do it right away? I planned to go down to the pasture first thing and help Pete catch the lambs."

"You'd better **bustle** around and bring up the water first."

"How many buckets do I have to bring?"

"How many buckets does it hold? You may as well fill it."

"How full must I make it?"

Mother laughed. "Must I **specify?** How full is *full,* David?"

The boy grinned **reluctantly,** then sighed deeply. "I just hate that job, Mother. Seems like that's all I ever do. And I always wind up sopping wet and too worn out to do anything else. It takes so long."

"Doing it this morning won't take any longer than doing it this afternoon. Then you can play in peace. Let me tell you a little proverb, David."

David did not reply. He wasn't so sure about some of Mother's little proverbs—especially when they pertained to work. And he didn't like the way she always made him repeat those proverbs after her.

Some of her proverbs came from the Bible. He believed those, of course. Others came from Benjamin Franklin. He could understand them easily enough and they made sense.

But he **suspected** that Mother made up some of her little proverbs. Those he didn't always like.

"Listen to this, David, 'An unpleasant task will make you happy if you do it sooner and better than necessary.' —Oh, there's Father waiting for me. Good-bye, dear. Look for us around six o'clock." And Mother bustled out the door.

David sighed deeply as he watched the carriage rattle out the lane. At least he didn't have to repeat Mother's proverb after her this time. But he found himself saying it anyhow. *An unpleasant task will make you happy if you do it sooner and better than necessary.*

That proverb sounded like one of Mother's made-up ones— one he certainly didn't agree with. Under no **circumstances** could he associate happiness with filling the water barrel, no matter when or how he did it.

True, he enjoyed their new house. It had taken a long time to build, for Father had done most of the work himself. Even yet, everything was not finished.

The well, for example. Father had not had time to dig a well, nor did he have money for the pipes to bring water into the house.

Instead, he had mounted a barrel on a sturdy platform at the kitchen sink. Mother could then draw water from a spigot at the bottom. The job of keeping water in the barrel fell to David.

Now David pulled the step stool over to the sink and climbed up. Leaning over the rim he tried to see how much water remained. Far below he saw the reflection of his face looking up at him.

"Nearly empty," he said with a sigh. Must he waste all the lovely morning carrying water while the hired man had the fun of working with the new lambs?

David backed down the steps and got the bucket from under the sink. He'd carry five buckets to get a good start, then go help Pete.

Five times he trudged to the spring and back. Five times he hoisted the full bucket over the rim of the barrel and listened to the splashing of the water as he poured it in.

"It won't matter if I don't finish it until this afternoon," he told himself. "It can't make any difference to Mother, just as long as I do it before she gets home."

Then he remembered that he had **calculated** that way one other time, and it hadn't worked out as he had thought.

His parents had gone to town and he had promised to fill the water barrel so Mother could wash clothes first thing in the morning. He had begun with enthusiasm, but before long had grown weary, and decided to quit for a while. After all, he had the rest of the afternoon and all evening for the unpleasant job.

When his parents returned, instead of having all evening to carry water, he had to go with Father to haul lumber. And that had taken until after dark. Mother hadn't gotten her wash started until the middle of the morning. That time he certainly would have been happy had he done his job sooner than necessary.

David stopped. A look of surprise crossed his face. Reluctantly he admitted that that experience proved the truth of Mother's proverb—at least the part about doing an unpleasant job *sooner* than necessary.

But the second part about doing it *better* than necessary would mean he would have to fill the despised water barrel fuller than ever. Mother never specified how much water he had to carry—just so she had all the water she needed. He usually stopped carrying water as soon as he thought she had enough to last awhile. Now he calculated it would take him at least an hour to do it "better than necessary."

"Doing it *better* simply means more work," declared David. "How could more work make you happy? That part of Mother's proverb can't possibly be true."

When David looked toward the barn he saw that Pete had finished with the lambs and had gone to mend fence in the south pasture. Wild blueberries grew thick down there. He'd go and help Pete for a while and get his fill of blueberries. Then he'd come back and fill that old barrel to running over. He'd prove that doing an unpleasant task better than necessary did *not* make you happy.

David set down his bucket and started on a run for the south pasture. But then he slowed to a walk, and finally stopped altogether. A burning curiosity had taken hold of him. Could that proverb be true? No, he didn't believe it, and here was his chance to prove it. Without a doubt, filling that barrel was an unpleasant task. He'd do it "sooner and better than necessary" and explode that proverb to smithereens.

A long time later, a hot, exhausted David climbed the step stool one last time. As he peered over the edge of the barrel, the reflection of his red sweated face met him only inches away. He lifted the bucket and poured a slow stream onto that smooth surface. Suddenly a trickle of water broke over the rim and ran down the side of the barrel.

David leaped off the stool with a shout of joy. "Whoopee! Full and running over! And it's not even dinner time! Wait till I tell Pete. Wait till Father and Mother see this! I won't have to carry water for two whole days."

David's weariness had vanished. He dropped the bucket in the sink. Then stopped. An odd look of mingled astonishment and disbelief crossed his face. "An unpleasant task will make you happy if you do it sooner and better than necessary," he whispered. "Isn't that queer? It really does. How did Mother know that?"

David grabbed a bowl from the cupboard. "I've the whole afternoon to do as I please. I'll pick enough blueberries for supper and help Pete fix the fence, and still have time for play."

An hour later found David helping Pete. He kept glancing with deep satisfaction toward the big bowl of blueberries sitting in the shade of a bush. The way he calculated, even after they ate some with cream for supper, there'd be enough for a pie. He could hardly wait until his parents returned.

"David, where's that smoke coming from?" Pete's excited voice interrupted the boy's contented thoughts.

David joined the hired man on the fence and shaded his eyes. "It's coming from the cellar windows on this side!"

Without another word Pete started at top speed across the field with David at his heels. When they burst into the house they found smoke seeping out around the door to the cellar. Pete jerked it open and plunged down, only to return choking and gasping for breath.

"The hose from the barn, boy—run! The lumber down there is smoldering." He grabbed the bucket from the sink and began filling it. In a minute David panted back dragging the hose. He watched Pete screw one end onto the spigot under the water barrel and turn it wide open. He watched him tie a wet towel over his nose and mouth. Then with a muffled, "Stay right here unless I call," he plunged down the cellar steps again, dragging the hose.

David could hardly endure the inactivity. First he stood as near the cellar door as possible, listening to Pete tumbling things around below. But the smoke drove him back. Then he climbed up to peer anxiously into the water barrel, watching the water level slowly receding. Suppose the barrel ran dry. Then they'd have to bring water from the spring. He ought to be hauling some right now, just in case.

But then he remembered the hired man had said, "Stay right here unless I call." Reluctantly he obeyed. Did Pete fear he might be overcome with smoke? David crawled to the cellar door and shouted, "Pete!"

Then Pete's voice close to the top of the steps startled him, "I'm coming, boy."

For ten minutes the hired man lay on the grass outside, gasping for breath and coughing. Black with smoke from head to foot, he could not talk for a long time. Then he rolled over and sat up.

"Close shave, David. There for a while I thought the house would go—all that lumber afire. Must have been started by spontaneous combustion in that pile of oily rags in the corner. How did it happen that we had so much water? I kept praying we wouldn't run out. I knew we could save the house if that barrel didn't run dry. A little bit less and I couldn't have gotten ahead of it."

"I filled it full and running over this morning," said David.

"Well, let me tell you then—you saved this nice brand-new house of your pa's from burning to a cinder."

"I think *you* saved it, Pete," said David. "All I did was fill the barrel. And I wouldn't have done that if I hadn't been trying to prove Mother's proverb wrong. And if Father hadn't built the water barrel, we'd have had to carry water from the spring. You and I could never have done that."

"Guess we'd better say God saved the house. The rest of us just helped a little."

And David, with a little thrill of happy thankfulness, agreed.

"Behold, the Lord's hand is not shortened, that it cannot save; neither his ear heavy, that it cannot hear."   Isaiah 59:1

In or Out?

After talking it over, James and Mary decided that just this once they could take care of their children better than God could.

"Well, perhaps we ought at least to bar our door, for the sake of the children." Mary Tyler spoke reluctantly, and there was a note of uncertainty in her voice.

"Perhaps so," replied James Tyler. "It seems to me every man within five miles has **upbraided** me for not protecting my children."

Mary glanced with troubled eyes at the face of her husband, as they sat before the fire in their little cabin. She knew that he, too, was remembering the uncertain days since the outbreak of the war. Time and again there had been reports that the French soldiers had **incited** the Indians to burn the cabins of the settlers and **massacre** whole families. Despite these reports, the Tylers had lived, as before, on friendly terms with their neighbors, both Indians and white men. When massacres had occurred in nearby settlements, they had still continued to

65

leave out the latchstring, the leather thong that enabled a person outside the door to lift the latch and enter.

The Tylers had trusted entirely to the protection of their heavenly Father and had refused to arm themselves or even to lock their door. Now they had reliable word that the Indians were coming to destroy their settlement. Neighbors urged that they had no right to **imperil** the lives of their children by such foolhardiness—that they should protect themselves.

"But is it really protection?" Mary **queried,** as now they sat alone in their cabin.

"At least," responded James, "we shall be doing what most people consider safest."

For what seemed a long time, they sat gazing at the fire.

The silence was broken only by the moaning of the wind in the pine trees and the crackling of the logs on the hearth. For the first time in all the dark days, Mary felt afraid. She stirred uneasily and cast a furtive glance around the shadowy room.

James rose and lighted the candle. He crossed the room and stood for a moment uncertainly beside the outside door. Then, with a deep sigh, he pulled in the leather thong, fastened the latch securely, and prepared for bed.

That night James tossed restlessly. Every time one of the children stirred or a branch scraped the roof, he would start violently, and fall back **unnerved.** He tried to calm himself by repeating verses from the Bible, but instead of the usual comfort, the words only brought a challenge to his excited brain. "Why are ye fearful, O ye of little faith?" "Take the shield of faith, wherewith ye shall be able to quench all the fiery darts of the wicked."

"Mary," he whispered at last, "art thou awake?"

"Yes, James," she replied, "I have not slept. I have tried to pray, and always the answer has been, 'Behold, the Lord's hand is not shortened, that it cannot save.'"

"Thou art right, Mary, the Lord's hand is not shortened and we did wrong to pull in the latchstring. Shall we put our trust entirely in Him?"

"Aye, James, I should feel much safer so," she replied.

Quickly James opened the door and pulled the leather thong through to the outside. Then he lay down again and both enjoyed such a sense of peace and security as they had not felt for hours.

Suddenly, just as they were about to drop off to sleep, they heard a blood-curdling war-whoop. A few seconds later the moccasined footsteps of several men passed the window and stopped in front of the door. The latch clicked and the door swung open. By the dim light from the embers on the hearth,

James could see seven Indians in full war paint. They motioned and talked to each other and then silently pulled the door shut and disappeared into the night.

In the morning when James and Mary went to check on their neighbors, they found only the smoking ruins of their cabins.

Years later, when the war was over, the government of the United States appointed James Tyler as a representative to an Indian conference. One day he told this story to all those assembled. In reply, an Indian arose and said: "I was one of those Indians. We crept up in night. We meant to burn and kill. We found latchstring out. We said, 'No burn this house. No kill these people. They do us no harm. They trust Great Spirit.'"

Indian Names

Ye say they all have passed away,
   That noble race and brave;
That their light canoes have vanished
   From off the crested wave;

That, mid the forests where they roamed,   5
   There rings no hunters' shout;
But their name is on your waters,
   Ye may not wash it out.

'Tis where Ontario's billow
   Like ocean's surge is curled,   10
Where strong Niagara's thunders wake
   The echo of the world,

Where red Missouri bringeth
   Rich tribute from the west,
And Rappahannock sweetly sleeps   15
   On green Virginia's breast.

–Lydia Huntly Sigourney, *Abridged*

"Defend the poor and fatherless: do justice to the afflicted and needy."

Psalm 82:3

The Bell of Atri

Here is a story your great-grandparents probably read when they were in school.

Many years ago the **ancient** town of Atri[1] straggled halfway up a steep slope in Italy. One morning the citizens noticed workmen constructing something in the very center of the square.

Inquiry satisfied no one, for to every question the workmen replied, "Our king commanded it. We dare tell nothing."

Every day idle townspeople loitered to watch. Busy citizens slowed their hurried pace when they neared the site.

What kind of building could the king want in the center of the square? Opinions fluttered back and forth like nervous butterflies.

Eventually the **structure** took on the form of a tower. That set tongues wagging faster than the tail of a happy puppy. Questions buzzed like bees around the ears of the workmen. They only shook their heads. "The king has commanded it. We dare not tell." But then they added, "You shall soon find out."

Atri – ä′ trē

After that, each day brought more citizens to loiter near the new structure. Curiosity rose higher and higher.

On the day the workmen finished the roof of the tower, the whole town of Atri had gathered to watch. Then men arrived bearing a beautiful shining bell. They carried it up into the tower and hung it under the roof. To the bell they attached a twisted **hempen** rope that dangled almost to the ground.

"A bell tower!" the people shouted. Now they knew. But why? Why would the king want a bell tower in the center of the square? No one ventured an answer to that question.

Suddenly someone shouted, "Make way for the king!"

Other voices took up the cry, "Make way for the king!"

Then everyone saw their king approaching on foot.

"He has come to ring the bell and explain its purpose," whispered the people to each other.

A path opened through the crowd and silence fell as the king walked to the foot of the tower. But he did not ring the bell. He began to speak. "My people, I had this tower built for you. I give the bell to you. It is the Bell of **Justice.** You may ring the bell whenever you need justice.

"If anyone wrongs you, come and pull the rope to ring the bell. Then the judges will gather here and listen to your case. They will see that justice is given you. They will punish the one who has wronged you.

"But do not accuse anyone falsely, or *you* will be the one to be punished. Accusing your neighbor falsely is just as wrong as any other wrong.

"Rich and poor, old and young, big and little may ring the bell. The rope is long enough for a child to reach. But no one must touch the rope unless he believes he has been wronged."

Many years rolled over the town of Atri. Many times the Bell of Justice pealed out from the tower in the square:

> Ding-dong—some—one
> Ding-dong—has—done
> Ding-dong—me—wrong.
> Ding-dong—Oh—come
> Ding-dong—and—judge
> Ding-dong—my—case.

Each time the judges hurried to the square to hear the case of the one who had rung the Bell of Justice. Other people came too, because they wanted to see who had wronged his fellow citizen. The judges righted many wrongs. They punished many wrong-doers.

Sometimes the judges found that the one who rang the bell was accusing another falsely. Then they punished the one who rang the bell. He left the square **humiliated** in the eyes of all who had gathered.

A wonderful thing began to happen in Atri. People began treating each other more kindly. They stopped cheating and stealing from each other. Everyone dreaded the humiliation of being called to the square by the Bell of Justice. They dreaded being punished in public for wronging a fellow citizen.

People also learned not to falsely accuse their neighbors. They thought twice before ringing the bell lest the judges punish them before all the people. Many who felt sure a person had wronged them decided to simply forgive and forget about it. They feared if they rang the bell and demanded justice, the judges might say they had falsely accused the other person.

Little by little the hempen bell rope grew worn and frazzled. It became shorter and shorter with use until only a man could reach it. No one paid much attention, for few needed to ring the bell anymore. Many of the people of Atri had learned to forgive each other and to settle their own disputes peaceably rather than risk being called to the public square by the Bell of Justice.

However, one day a man, seeing the short rope, said to himself, "That will never do. Our king said that the tiniest child should be able to ring the bell. Perchance today a little one would need justice. He could not reach the rope."

The man went to a nearby vineyard and cut a long

grapevine. This he knotted securely to the frayed end of the bell rope, and went away satisfied.

On the hillside above Atri stood the mansion of a rich **miser** called Sir Squeeze-gold. He had another name, of course, but the citizens of Atri had long forgotten it. In his youth Sir Squeeze-gold had faithfully served the king as a brave knight, making long journeys on his faithful horse.

The man had eventually grown too old to serve as a knight. Now he wanted to do nothing but sit in his mansion, count his gold, and devise ways to keep from spending a single coin.

His horse had grown old also. At first Sir Squeeze-gold used him to plow the veg- etable garden and drag firewood from the for- est. To save time, he forced the beast to haul such huge loads that eventually the faithful animal became hope- lessly lame.

Angrily Sir Squeeze- gold drove the limping creature into a rocky pasture, all the while wondering, *Now how will I get firewood?*

For days the miser sat brooding over his

problem. How could he get fuel from his forest without paying someone to cut and haul it for him?

No way offered itself, and Sir Squeeze-gold blamed the horse. He watched it growing thinner day by day in the rocky pasture. Instead of pitying the faithful creature who had helped him gain his riches, he began to resent that the broken-down animal ate his grass without doing any work in return.

One day he opened the gate and chased the scrawny beast out. He whacked its bony hip as it hobbled past him into the road that led down to the town. "Go and eat off someone else," he shouted.

All in Atri heard the Bell of Justice that quiet afternoon.

> Ding-dong—some—one
> Ding-dong—has—done
> Ding-dong—me—wrong.
> Ding-dong—Oh—come
> Ding-dong—and—judge
> Ding-dong—my—case.

The judges and the entire town rushed to the square. No one had rung the bell for a long time.

There stood a skinny horse hungrily devouring the grapevine tied to the bell rope.

"The horse belongs to Sir Squeeze-gold," exclaimed one.

"Look how thin the poor beast is," cried another.

"When young and strong he served his master faithfully."

"And helped him earn all his wealth."

"Now his master refuses to care for him."

"And has turned him out because he can work no longer."

"For shame! For shame!" a dozen indignant voices cried.

And all the while the poor old horse munched away on the grapevine, and the Bell of Justice kept on ringing:

Ding-dong—some—one
Ding-dong—has—done
Ding-dong—me—wrong.
Ding-dong—Oh—come
Ding-dong—and—judge
Ding-dong—my—case.

"Bring the miser to the square," ordered the judges. Frightened and humiliated beyond speech, Sir Squeeze-gold stood with bowed head before the judges and all the people of Atri.

"Your horse has called for justice, and he shall have it," the judges declared.

For a while they did not know how to guarantee that the old horse would receive kind treatment. Then one man stepped forward. "Let me have the horse. I will care for him if Sir Squeeze-gold pays me."

"Sir Squeeze-gold *will* pay you," stated the judges. "He will pay you for a warm stall as well as sweet hay and grain for the horse as long as he lives.

"Our king hung the bell to provide justice for all. We will see that even a horse will receive justice if he rings the Bell of Justice."

The old miser stumbled away, but all the people shouted for joy.

– James Baldwin

"He that passeth by, and meddleth with strife belonging not to him, is like one that taketh a dog by the ears."   Proverbs 26:17

Test Room

If you had been a fifth grader a hundred years ago, you might have studied the following story in your reader. The introduction here is different from the one in McGuffey's Fifth Reader, *but the story itself is exactly as fifth graders read it a century ago.*

Do you find this story harder to read than the other stories in your book? Do you think children today need the lesson it teaches?

Introduction

A wealthy old gentleman lived in a mansion called Elm Tree Hall. Everyone loved him because he used his money to help the old, the poor, and the sick around him. No beggar ever left his door without a **generous** handout.

Children loved him too, for he enjoyed working and talking and playing with young people.

However, there was one kind of child he could not endure. He despised a child who did not control his curiosity, but **meddled** with things he had no business touching.

He used to say, "A boy who will peep into a drawer in someone else's house will be tempted to take something from it. A boy who will sneak a piece of candy will steal money."

Now it came to pass that this old gentleman wanted a boy to help him at his meals and do odd jobs around Elm Tree Hall. Twenty boys applied for the position because they knew the old gentleman would pay generous wages.

However, the old gentleman did not want a boy in Elm Tree Hall who would open doors and peep into cupboards and drawers out of curiosity. He wanted someone who would resist the temptation to meddle or to help himself to something that didn't belong to him, even if it had little value. He had no intention of hiring such a boy. But how could he discover beforehand what kind of character a boy possessed?

The old gentleman, being clever, as well as generous and kind, prepared a room in which to test the **applicants.** He planned to hire the first boy who passed the test and proved he did not have a curious, prying disposition.

As each applicant arrived at Elm Tree Hall for an **interview,** a servant ushered him into the test room. Each was told, "Just wait here until the old gentleman sends for you."

Do Not Meddle

First, Charles Brown was sent into the room and told that he would have to wait a little. So Charles sat down on a chair near the door. For some time he was very quiet, and looked about him, but there seemed to be so many curious things in the room that at last he got up to peep at them.

On the table was placed a dish cover, and Charles wanted badly to know what was under it, but he felt afraid of lifting it up. Bad habits are strong things; and, as Charles was of a curious disposition, he could not withstand the temptation of taking one peep. So he lifted up the cover.

This turned out to be a sad affair; for under the dish cover was a heap of very light feathers; part of the feathers, drawn up by a current of air, flew about the room, and Charles, in his fright, putting the cover down hastily, puffed the rest of them off the table.

What was to be done? Charles began to pick up the feathers one by one; but the old gentleman, who was in an **adjoining** room, hearing a scuffle, and guessing the cause of it, entered the room, to the consternation of Charles Brown, who was very soon dismissed as a boy who had not **principle** enough to resist even a slight temptation.

When the room was once more arranged, Henry Wilkins was placed there until such a time as he should be sent for. No sooner was he left to himself than his attention was attracted by a plate of fine, ripe cherries. Now Henry was uncommonly fond of cherries, and he thought it would be impossible to miss one cherry among so many. He looked and longed, and longed and looked, for some time, and just as he had got off his seat to take one, he heard, as he thought, a foot coming to the door; but no, it was a false alarm.

Taking fresh courage, he went cautiously and took a very fine cherry, for he was determined to take but one, and put it into his mouth. It was excellent; and then he persuaded himself that he ran no risk in taking another; this he did, and hastily popped it into his mouth.

Now, the old gentleman had placed a few artificial cherries at the top of the others, filled with cayenne pepper; one of these Henry had unfortunately taken, and it made his mouth smart and burn most intolerably. The old gentleman heard him coughing, and knew very well what was the matter. The boy that would take what did not belong to him, if no more than a cherry, was not the boy for him. Henry Wilkins was sent about his business without delay, with his mouth almost as hot as if he had put a burning coal into it.

Rufus Wilson was next introduced into the room and left to himself; but he had not been there ten minutes before he began to move from one place to another. He was of a bold resolute temper, but not overburdened with principle; for if he could have opened every cupboard, closet, and drawer in the house, without being found out, he would have done it directly.

Having looked around the room, he noticed a drawer to the table, and made up his mind to peep therein. But no sooner did he lay hold of the drawer knob than he set a large bell ringing, which was concealed under the table. The old gentleman immediately answered the summons, and entered the room.

Rufus was so startled by the sudden ringing of the bell, that all his impudence could not support him. He looked as though any one might knock him down with a feather. The old gentleman asked him if he had rung the bell because he wanted anything. Rufus was much confused, and stammered, and tried to excuse himself, but all to no purpose, for it did not prevent him from being ordered off the premises.

George Jones was then shown into the room by an old steward; and being of a cautious disposition, he touched nothing, but only looked at the things about him. At last he saw that a closet door was open a little, and, thinking it would be impossible for any one to know that he had opened it a little more, he very cautiously opened it an inch further, looking down at the bottom of the door, that it might not catch against anything and make a noise.

Now had he looked at the top, instead of the bottom, it might have been better for him; for to the top of the door was fastened a plug, which filled up the hole of a small barrel of shot. He ventured to open the door another inch, and then another, till, the plug being pulled out of the barrel, the leaden shot began to pour out at a strange rate. At the bottom of the closet was placed a tin pan, and the shot falling upon this pan made such a clatter that George was frightened half out of his senses.

The old gentleman soon came into the room to inquire what was the matter, and there he found George nearly as pale as a sheet. George was soon dismissed.

It now became the turn of Albert Jenkins to be put into the room. The other boys had been sent to their homes by different ways, and no one knew what the experience of the other had been in the room of trial.

On the table stood a small round box, with a screw top to it, and Albert, thinking it contained something curious, could not be easy without unscrewing the top; but no sooner did he do this than out bounced an artificial snake, full a yard long, and fell upon his arm. He started back, and uttered a scream which brought the old gentleman to his elbow. There stood Albert, with the bottom of the box in one hand, and the top in the other, and the snake on the floor.

"Come, come," said the old gentleman, "one snake is quite enough to have in the house at a time; therefore, the sooner you are gone the better." With that he dismissed him, without waiting a moment for his reply.

William Smith next entered the room, and being left alone soon began to amuse himself in looking at the curiosities around him. William was not only curious and prying, but dishonest, too, and observing that the key was left in the drawer of a bookcase, he stepped on tiptoe in that direction. The key had a wire fastened to it, which communicated with an electrical machine, and William received such a shock as he was not likely to forget. No sooner did he sufficiently recover himself to walk, than he was told to leave the house, and let other people lock and unlock their own drawers.

The other boy was Harry Gordon, and though he was left in the room full twenty minutes, he never during that time stirred from his chair. Harry had eyes in his head as well as the others, but he had more integrity in his heart; neither the dish cover, the cherries, the drawer knob, the closet door, the round box, nor the key tempted him to rise from his seat; and the consequence was that, in half an hour after, he was engaged in the service of the old gentleman at Elm Tree Hall. He followed his good old master to his grave, and received a large legacy for his upright conduct in his service.

In the story you just read, some boys were looking for a job. In this poem, a lad wishes he could have been an apprentice for a certain Carpenter. Do you know who that carpenter was?

In the Carpenter Shop

I wish I had been His apprentice,
    To see Him each morning at seven,
As he tossed His gray tunic about Him,
    The Master of earth and of heaven.

When He lifted the lid of His work-chest   5
    And opened His carpenter's kit,
And looked at His chisels and augers,
    And took the bright tools out of it;

When He gazed at the rising sun tinting
    The dew on the opening flowers,   10
And he smiled at the thought of His Father
    Whose love floods this fair world of ours.

When He fastened the apron about Him,
    And put on His workingman's cap,
And grasped the smooth haft of His hammer   15
    To give the bent woodwork a tap,

Saying, "Lad, let us finish this ox yoke,
    The farmer must finish his crop."
Oh, I wish I had been His apprentice
    And worked in the Nazareth shop.   20

—Author Unknown

"As cold waters to a thirsty soul, so is good news from a far country."

Proverbs 25:25

George Makes a Way
Part 1

What world-famous scientist refused an invitation to work with Thomas Edison? Who pulled southern farmers out of poverty by showing them how to raise something besides cotton? Who found over a hundred uses for the sweet potato? Who developed more than three hundred products that could be made from peanuts? Who struggled all his life to learn more but gave God the credit for everything he had accomplished?

"So this is where you come when you slip away from the house at four o'clock of a morning?"

The little black boy sat back on his heels and smiled shyly up at the white man peering through the bushes.

"Yes, sir, Uncle Mose. I've got to tend my flowers—and look at this. It just opened. The bulb 'tweren't more than a **runt** when I stuck it in." The youngster turned up a tiger lily blossom. "And see here." He pointed to a green spear poking through the leaves. "It looked 'most dead when I **transplanted** it, but it's growing after all."

"You've made a beautiful spot all hidden away here in the woods," exclaimed Mr. Carver, observing the collection of flowers and ferns bordered by a fence of stout branches. "Where did you get them all?"

"Found some in the woods and transplanted them. Got slips and cuttings and seeds from Aunt Susan and the neighbors. This is my secret garden."

"Plants sure grow for you, George."

"That's 'cause I love 'em and talk to 'em and nurse 'em along when they get sick. But I wish I knew their real names. I mean to learn to read. Then I could find out the names of everything.

"I'm aiming to go to that school down the road and learn how to read. Reckon I could start next week, Uncle Mose?"

Moses Carver gazed off into the woods for a long moment. With a **wrench** of his heart, he knew he had to explain to this happy little Negro boy the ugly fact of race **prejudice**. Then he said, "You can't do that, George."

"Oh, but I could, Uncle Mose. It's just a couple miles. I want to learn about things—why bees like clover best, what makes it rain, how pink and yellow flowers all grow from the same dirt, how the seeds get inside a pumpkin. All that is written down in books somewhere. If I learn to read, I can find out about all of it."

"Yes, yes, George," interrupted Mr. Carver, "but—but—" he paused, embarrassed.

"But what, Uncle Mose?"

"That's a white school, George."

"I know." George looked puzzled.

"And you're colored."

"I know," the boy repeated, still puzzled.

"George," Mr. Carver's voice grew sad and gentle. "You have been our boy since you were born. You'll always be our boy. But you are too young yet to know about most people in this world. I'm sorry, but those white folks don't want colored children in their school."

Stunned, the little boy stared up at the man. "But why, Uncle Mose? I know God made me black and you white, same as He made some dogs black and some white. He made some roses red and some yellow and some pink. They are all roses. Black and white people are all just people, aren't they? What difference does that make?"

"It doesn't make any difference to God," answered Mr. Carver, "but it does make a difference to some white people. You're colored and white folks won't let you go to their school. That's settled."

And that is how Carver's George learned about race prejudice.

Moses Carver walked through the woods toward the house remembering all that led up to this day. In Diamond Grove, Missouri, and in the rest of the south, farmers had no tractors. All machinery was powered by horse or mule. At that time in the middle of the 1800s, southern farmers thought they couldn't make a living without the free help of black slaves.

Moses Carver didn't hold with slavery. He didn't believe in "causing money to pass over the body of another human." That's what they said when a man bought another person just like he bought a horse and wagon.

Mose did all his own farm work, or hired a man to help him. But his wife Susan stayed so weak and lonely after the death of their one baby girl that Moses knew she needed help and companionship.

He could find no one to hire, so he bought thirteen-year-old Mary from a neighbor for $700. Though a slave, Mary was bright and cheerful and soon became one of the family. Later when she married, Mose and Susan Carver loved and cared for her children as if they were their own.

Mary's husband remained a slave on a neighboring plantation and one day was killed in a logging accident, so little George never remembered his father. He considered Mose and Susan Carver his parents, for his mother, too, had disappeared before he could remember her.

In those days gangs of masked men rode around the countryside stealing slaves. They carried these slaves far off and sold them again before their owners could trail them.

One bitter December night some of these bushwhackers appeared at the Carver home. They seized Mary, wrenched her sickly infant son from her arms, and galloped off into the darkness with them both.

Moses Carver immediately hired a man to pursue the night riders, a difficult task in those days of no telephones, cars, or good roads. After a week, the Carvers feared that the man had run off with the money and hadn't even tried to find Mary and her baby.

But one cold rainy night the man appeared at the house, soaking wet and discouraged. "Sorry, I couldn't bring the girl. I never could catch up with 'em. Rode clear to Arkansas and lost their trail. Then some people told me they went north. Some others said south. This is all I got." The man pulled a dirty bundle from under his dripping coat and held it out toward Susan. "They left the young 'un with some women. It's just a runt. Ain't worth nuthin'. Don't know if it's even alive."

"Mary's baby!" With a cry, Susan grabbed the bundle. She pulled back the cold wet wrappings and held the scrawny little body close to the fire.

So Susan Carver saved Mary's baby, though some wondered why she bothered. They called him George—Carver's George.

The first several years no one but Susan thought he would live. She nursed him day and night through every childhood ailment that a baby could catch. And always he coughed a deep rending cough. Eventually that wrenching cough so damaged his voice that it always sounded high-pitched and weak. More than that, the little boy stammered badly. Most people couldn't understand him when he spoke, but he sang his own happy made-up songs from morning till night.

The Civil War had set the slaves free, but that meant nothing to Carver's George. He had never known he was a slave. Uncle Mose and Aunt Susan had never been his owners. They were his family.

From a little boy, George hungered to know about all he saw. "How does cotton grow, Uncle Mose? Why does the sun go down over there and come up over here?"

His black eyes watched everything closely. He wanted to try everything he saw others doing. "Let me try that," he begged

Uncle Mose after watching him plow the furrows in the garden with the big mule.

But George's thin arms and spindly legs weren't strong enough to do heavy farm work, no matter how hard he tried.

"I can do that," he told Aunt Susan after watching her spinning or knitting or making candles. His clever fingers and eagerness to work soon made him able to do almost anything Aunt Susan did. Cooking, cleaning, washing, ironing, sewing, soap-making—he learned to do it all and never once cared about its being women's work.

People soon discovered that Carver's George had a way with plants. He somehow knew what ailed a sickly rosebush or geranium. "Put it in the sun," or "Cut it back a little," or "Don't water it so much." Plants recovered when people followed George's advice.

In his secret glade in the woods, George planted and transplanted. He experimented with different seeds in different soils. He discovered the tiny worms and insects that made plants sicken and die. And all the time his eager little heart burned with a desire to learn more and more.

Then he had discovered the little school in town. A great hope leaped up. He could learn to read! He clutched that dream like a thirsty man would seize a cup of cold water. But now Uncle Mose's words knocked that cup from him before he could taste one drop. "You're colored. White folks won't let you go to their school. That's settled." The ugly fact of race prejudice dared him to argue with it.

George turned back to his secret garden whispering, "But I *will* learn how to read! I will! I *will!*"

What Uncle Mose told Aunt Susan George never knew. But from her trunk she dug a copy of *Webster's Speller*. She taught him the alphabet. In a few weeks George had memorized the whole book even though he didn't know what all the words meant.

In the evenings Uncle Mose held the small brown hand in his big rough paw and taught him to write his name.

Lincoln School for Colored Children! Only by accident had Carver's George discovered it. One day in the town of Neosho, eight miles from Diamond Grove, George noticed a log shanty. A line of colored children straggled through the doorway, followed by the closing of the door.

Drawing closer, George heard the sing-song voices of the children spelling words. A school! This must be a school for colored children!!

At home George stammered out what he had discovered. "Uncle Mose! It's a school for colored children. I must go."

"But, George, how can you? Where would you stay? What would you eat? Where'd you sleep?"

"I'll find me a place. I can work. I can sweep and tote water. I can wash and iron. I can cook and do dishes. I must go, Uncle Mose."

The white man looked long into the eager little brown face and pleading black eyes. Finally he said, "You aren't a slave, George. You don't belong to me. I don't have the money to help you, but I can't stop you, either. You're just a little feller. I don't see how you can make out."

One afternoon a day or so later Carver's George started down the dusty road toward Neosho. In a bundle he carried his extra shirt and a supply of corn dodgers Aunt Susan had baked for him. Uncle Mose and Aunt Susan watched from the gate till, with a final wave, he turned the bend.

"He's such a little feller, not even twelve yet," Aunt Susan said with tears running down her cheeks. "He's transplanting himself just like he did all those flowers in his secret glade. But he doesn't know how hard and cruel the world is."

"Well, he knows he can come home any time," Uncle Mose comforted her. He paused, then went on, "But I have a feeling he won't be back."

Toward evening Carver's George arrived in Neosho. He immediately sought out the shanty where he had seen the children entering. He walked around it imagining himself inside learning to read. This was his school where he would learn to read and then find out all the things he wanted to know.

Aunt Susan's corn dodgers took away the empty feeling in his stomach. But a greater emptiness settled in his heart as he realized he knew no one in the whole town. And no one knew him.

He hung around the tumble-down little school house until almost dark, then slipped into a barn behind a nearby cabin. Weary from his eight-mile walk, and lonelier than he had ever felt in his life, he pulled himself up the ladder into the haymow and almost instantly fell asleep.

"My first day of school." That thought early the next morning drove all loneliness from George's heart. Nothing mattered but learning. Learning to read. Learning the names of flowers and trees. Learning why one bird built a nest on the ground and another in a tree.

He brushed every bit of hay from his clothes and smoothed them as best he could. Then he climbed down the ladder.

It was too early for school. But he didn't care. He settled himself on a woodpile across the fence to wait for the teacher to come and unlock the door.

"What'cha doin' here, boy?"

George turned. A thin colored lady stood at the back door of the little cabin. He scrambled off the wood pile and walked slowly toward her.

"I-I-I'm jes a-waitin' for the school to open. I've c-c-come to go to school."

"You've got a long wait. This is Saturday."

George gulped. He had paid no attention to the days.

"Where did you come from? What's your name? Who's your folks?"

George raised miserable eyes to the woman's face. He saw that for all her sharp words her eyes shone kindly on him.

"I'm from Diamond Grove. I'm Carver's George. Don't have any folks 'cept Mose and Susan Carver. Bushwhackers took my ma."

"My name's Mariah[1] Watkins. So you came here to go to school?"

"Yes, ma'am."

"Where are you planning to live?"

"I'll find a place where I can work and go to school. I can do 'most everything."

---

[1]Mariah – mə rī′ ə

"Say—you hungry, boy?" came the next question.

"Yes, ma'am."

"Well, wash up over there, then come on in."

George went to the pump she indicated. He washed his face, neck, hands, arms, and feet. Before long he found himself pouring molasses over hot golden biscuits.

George soon learned that Mariah Watkins washed clothes for a living. All that morning he carried water and kept the fire going under the kettles. He watched as Mariah rubbed and boiled and rinsed piles of clothes. He helped hang them on the lines.

"All the quality white folks bring their clothes to me," she told George.

At noon Andrew Watkins appeared for his dinner. He was a big man with **grizzled** hair and beard. He looked questioningly at the boy poking and stirring the snowy linens as they boiled in the huge black kettles in the yard.

Mariah put food on the table. From time to time George darted an anxious eye toward the open door. He could see husband and wife talking in low tones as they ate.

Then Mariah called him inside. "Would you want to stay with us? You can, if you work as good as you did this morning."

"Oh, ma'am," George said eagerly. "Yes, I would like to stay with you. But I can go to school, can't I?"

"Of course. Isn't that what you came for?"

Mr. Watkins smiled above his grizzled beard. "You can call me Uncle Andy and her Aunt Mariah. We're mighty glad to have you, son."

94

"Thank you," whispered George. "Thank you, Uncle Andy and Aunt Mariah. You won't ever be sorry you took me in." He turned quickly away so they wouldn't see the tears that suddenly filled his eyes. Until that moment Carver's George hadn't realized how worried he really was about where he would live while he attended school.

Before he went back to work, Uncle Andy nailed a blanket across a corner of the one-room cabin. Aunt Mariah laid down a rug. "This will be your place," she said.

"Thank you, ma'am," said George, putting his little bundle on the floor behind the curtain.

After breakfast the next morning, Aunt Mariah said, "You wash up good now, George. Put on your other shirt. It's soon time to go to church."

"To church, ma'am? I've never been to church. Uncle Mose didn't hold with church."

"Everyone goes to church from this house," boomed Uncle Andy.

Fear knotted George's stomach. His imagination had painted some rather frightful pictures of what people did in church.

But from the first joyful hymn that rolled from the throats of the little congregation, his fear dissolved into delightful enjoyment. How those colored folks could sing!

Then the preacher stood and told of the love that God had for all His creatures. That thought filled George's heart with a gratitude and awe that stayed with him the rest of his life.

That evening as they sat outside the cabin enjoying the cooling breezes as darkness came on, George said, "Aunt

Mariah, it was mighty lucky for me a-pickin' your woodpile to sit on yesterday."

"Don't you go calling that luck," said Aunt Mariah sharply. "God sent you to our yard. He has a work for you to do, and He chose Andrew and me to help."

"You reckon that's true?" asked George, in surprise. He had never heard of such a thing.

"Of course, it's true," put in Uncle Andy. "God has work for everybody to do, if they'd just listen hard enough to find out what it is. You keep a-listening and a-learning and sometime you'll know what God wants you to do."

On the rug behind the curtain that night Carver's George lay a long time thinking over Uncle Andy's words. "I wonder," he said to himself, "I wonder if that's true."

The next morning George could hardly wait for school to begin. Just as he climbed the fence, Aunt Mariah called after him, "Now don't tell that teacher your name is Carver's George. You're not a slave. You don't belong to Mr. Carver. You tell the teacher your name is George Carver, you hear?"

"Yes, ma'am," replied George, blinking his eyes at the thought. "George Carver. George Carver. George Carver," he whispered to himself, as he went toward the door.

Almost seventy-five pupils crowded into the little shack of a school house that morning. All sizes, all ages, all grades in the one room. The teacher, Mr. Frost, squeezed George onto an already-full bench of other first graders. He handed him a ragged reader and piece of a slate.

From that moment on, George's mind soaked up everything. Whatever grade Mr. Frost taught, whatever the subject, George

listened and remembered. The constant buzz of children studying, the squirming and shuffling on the uncomfortable benches
did not bother George.

In school at last! And sometime he would find out what God
wanted him to do.

— Ruth K. Hobbs

School Bell

Nine o'clock Bell!
Nine o'clock Bell!
All the small children and big ones as well,
Pulling their stockings up, snatching their hats,
Cheeking and grumbling and giving back-chats,   5
Laughing and quarreling, dropping their things,
These at a snail's pace and those upon wings,
Lagging behind a bit, running ahead,
Waiting at corners for lights to turn red,
    Some of them scurrying,   10
    Others not worrying,
Carelessly trudging or anxiously hurrying,
All through the streets they are coming pell-mell
    At the Nine o'clock
        Nine o'clock   15
        Nine o'clock
            Bell!

—Eleanor Farjeon

"For thy work shall be rewarded, saith the LORD."

Jeremiah 31:16

George Makes a Way
Part 2

George imagined that when he learned to read, nothing could stop him in his search for knowledge about the plants he loved. But before long he met a blockade on that road. Could he find his way around it, or would he give up his dream?

Eleven-year-old George Carver didn't stay in first grade long. His thirsty little mind **absorbed** every word the teacher said. He read and reread all the books the little school possessed until he knew them **thoroughly.**

Still thin and sickly, he cared nothing about recess. He stood around watching the others play and could hardly wait till the teacher rang the bell and he could get back to learning.

At noon he hopped across the fence to eat the good lunch Aunt Mariah always had waiting in the little cabin. Then he returned to the overcrowded schoolroom of **jostling** students to his books and slate.

After school he helped Aunt Mariah with laundry. He didn't mind doing women's work, for he had adopted a motto for himself. *Watch what people do with their hands. Observe and remember exactly what and how they do it. Then try it yourself as soon as you can, and practice, practice, practice.*

Aunt Mariah gave George another motto to live and work by. One day she told him, "Pay attention to what you are doing. I want things done just so for my customers. *Almost* perfect won't pass."

So George learned to wash and starch and iron a snowy petticoat so stiff it could stand up by itself. And from then on he held himself to that standard—*Almost* perfect won't pass. That's the way he did his lessons. That's the way he did every job, thoroughly and as nearly perfect as he possibly could.

One evening several years later, George stood at the open window of the cabin. The day had been warm for that time of winter. He stood there daydreaming for a long time with his head propped on his hands. His dark eyes gazed unseeing beyond the little schoolhouse next door.

Finally he turned back into the room. "Uncle Andy, I've learned everything Mr. Frost can teach me. He says I know everything a colored person needs to get along in a white man's world. He says colored folks aren't smart enough to learn like white folks."

Uncle Andy snorted. "And him a colored man himself! You tell that teacher that God made a colored man's brain no different than a white man's. Neither one is much good unless you use it."

"There's a whole lot more to know than Mr. Frost knows, son. You'll have to go on. You'll have to keep going on until

you find out what God wants you to do," Aunt Mariah put in.

"But there's no other school in Neosho. I'll have to go some-where else," protested George.

"I heard the Smiths are moving to Kansas," said Uncle Andy slowly. "Probably there is a school out there. But winter isn't over. This kind of weather can't be good for that cough of yours. You might get sick again. What would you do without Aunt Mariah to nurse you?"

"Uncle Andy, sometimes a flower does better when you transplant it. Maybe I need to be transplanted. It could be that in a different climate I'd grow stronger and get rid of my cough.

"Anyhow, I must find another school," he continued almost in **desperation.** "I thought Mr. Frost would know everything, but he didn't teach me anything about plants. I still don't know why things grow better in black soil than in yellow. I still don't know why cotton plants keep getting smaller and smaller in the same field every year. But I know that somewhere I can find the answers to all my questions."

"George, you'll have to make your own way in this world. Thank God you aren't a slave, but just remember, some white folks will keep on treating you like one. They **resent** all colored folks. They won't let you do anything but slave work. But don't let that bother you. No work is slave work unless you think it is. Be thankful for any work God gives you. A lot of white folks want us black folks to stay ignorant, so don't expect them to help you. But if you stay ignorant it's your own fault. Just because something's hard is no reason to quit," Aunt Mariah said in her short snappy way.

"I believe God wants you to go on learning, then come back and help our people. But work'll be hard to find in the winter. You can't be sleeping in barns up north. Why not stay here till spring?"

"God will lead me to something. He led me to your yard, didn't He, Aunt Mariah?" said George earnestly. "I've got to go when there's a way. Please let me ask the Smiths if I can ride along," begged George.

Reluctantly Uncle Andy and Aunt Mariah gave their consent, though they realized they had no authority to refuse his request.

"They said I may go with them," George announced excitedly several days later. "I can ride in the back of the wagon with the furniture and farm tools and chickens. But I must take my own food and not cause any trouble, or expect them to help me."

"Oh, George, can't you wait till warm weather? What if you can't find a place to stay? What if you don't find work? You've got to have money to buy school books. Kansas is full of white folks. They won't help you or care what happens to you."

"Aunt Mariah," George answered bravely. "You've told me there's always work for a body who's willing to tackle anything. White folks have money. They always want colored boys to do their work. I'll get along. I must go when I've got the chance."

"It will be mighty lonesome here without you, son," said Uncle Andy. "Remember, you can always come back." But as he said the words, **intuition** told him George would somehow make a way for himself and not return.

After four days of jostling along in the overloaded wagon, the Smiths arrived in Fort Scott, Kansas. On that January day in 1877 they stopped the tired team in the middle of the muddy street.

Young George Carver pulled himself from the sheltered nook he had made. Picking up his bundle, he climbed stiffly down over the wagon wheel. "Thank you, Mr. Smith," he said. "Much obliged for the ride."

Then he stood there shivering, hungry and scared, watching the Smiths rattle away.

Not a soul did George know in the city. He had no money, no work, no place to go. His brave words to Aunt Mariah did not sound so courageous now. Instead they sounded frighteningly foolish.

Then his dream returned—his dream of going on in school and learning about flowers and trees and crops. He must discover how God wanted him to help his people.

In the south in those days most Negroes stayed as poor and ignorant as they had been during slavery. The southern whites had lost the war. They had to free their slaves, but they deeply resented their former slaves trying to better themselves in any way. They were determined to "keep the Negro in his place," as they termed it.

Of course, George knew nothing about that as he stood with chattering teeth in Fort Scott, Kansas. However, he did realize with a sinking certainty that no one in the whole city knew or cared about his desperate need for food and shelter. No one except George Carver. He, himself, must do something about that. So off he started.

"Do you need a boy to carry wood and tend fires? I can scrub floors and wash dishes. I can do laundry and iron clothes. I'll do a good job of anything you want done, ma'am." George could not remember how often he made that speech at the back doors of white people's big fine houses in Fort Scott.

He could not remember how many doors had opened and closed in his face. Some were slammed before he even began talking. He had grown so cold he could hardly keep his teeth from chattering as he talked.

As the winter afternoon wore on he knew he would soon have to hunt for a barn or shed in which to spend the night before it grew too dark to see. He would try one more house.

The woman who opened the door listened to his speech as she eyed the thin teenager up and down.

"I don't need help in any of those things. But my cook just left. Can you cook?"

"Yes, ma'am," replied George promptly.

"Come in then. I'll give you a try, for I need help right now with supper."

After George had answered a dozen questions about his background, the lady said briskly, "I'm Mrs. Payne. Come out to the kitchen. The roast is in the oven. Should be nearly finished. You'll want to make gravy. My husband likes it pretty thick. And fry some of that winter squash. But you'd better start on the dried apple pie, so it can bake awhile. The apples are soaking in that bowl there. Biscuits, of course, after the pie's out of the oven. And coffee. My husband is very particular about his coffee. I hope you can make good coffee."

A faintness had come over George when he first stepped into the warm kitchen and smelled food. But with a great effort he steadied himself. Politely he answered Mrs. Payne's questions and absorbed every word she said.

Now the instructions for supper had left him in blank despair. He had not meant to lie to this lady. He *could* cook the way Aunt Mariah cooked—collard greens, black-eyed peas, skillet-fried corn bread, but . . .

Then his mind began working with the speed of desperation. Out from the bewildering jumble of new impressions, one thought pushed itself to the forefront. He must *not* lose this opportunity. He *couldn't!*

Pulling off his coat, he laid it and his bundle aside. He washed his hands thoroughly at what he decided, with swift intuition, was a pump over the sink, though he had never seen the like in his life.

As he put on the long white apron Mrs. Payne held out to him, he said earnestly. "Ma'am, I want to fix everything the way your husband likes it best. Could you show me just this first time the recipes you use and how you go about preparing everything?"

"That's a good idea, George," said Mrs. Payne. "People do have different recipes and ways of making things. Now this is how I make pie crust."

The lady took things from this cupboard and that. She pulled out drawers, talking all the while. She demonstrated how to boil the coffee, thicken the gravy, fry the squash, and make the biscuits.

George watched how her hands measured and mixed, stirred and rolled, turned and patted. His trap-like mind absorbed every word she said. He noted where she had gotten the utensils and ingredients, and thoroughly memorized most of the recipes she used.

Of course, the supper turned out fine, for Mrs. Payne had done it all. But George knew that the next time he could do it all by himself.

After supper George did not forget Aunt Mariah's motto: "*Almost* perfect won't pass." Another servant had served the meal and cleared the table. But George washed the dishes. Without being told, he filled the woodbox and banked the fire in the stove. He swept the floor and left the kitchen shining clean.

At last he picked up the night candle and went to the little room Mrs. Payne had showed him under the back stairs. He read for a while in the little Bible Aunt Mariah had given him for Christmas. And for just a minute he thought lonesomely about her and Uncle Andy. Then warmed and filled and deeply thankful, he stretched his exhausted frame out on the narrow cot and fell asleep.

—Ruth K. Hobbs

George learned the truth of this poem early in life. He learned it in the garden by growing things. How do you think he learned it in life?

Results and Roses

The man who wants a garden fair,
    Or small or very big,
With flowers growing here and there,
    Must bend his back and dig.

The things are mighty few on earth   5
    That wishes can attain.
Whate'er we want of any worth
    We've got to work to gain.

It matters not what goal you seek—
    Its secret here reposes: 10
You've got to dig from week to week
    To get Results or Roses.

                 –Edgar A. Guest

Tales Truly True

Words

Bright is the ring of words
    When the right man rings them,
Fair the fall of songs
    When the singer sings them.
Still they are caroled and said—
    On wings they are carried—
After the singer is dead
    And the maker buried.

–Robert Louis Stevenson

"I sought the Lord, and he heard me, and delivered me from all my fears."

Psalm 34:4

Zambezi Crisis

How do you decide when you must choose between two things that look equally impossible? Did God really mean for the missionary explorer to go ahead when angry natives threatened to kill them all?

Darkness had fallen on the camp of David Livingstone beside the Zambezi[1] River. The African forest crouched black and terrifying around them. The missionary explorer and his helpers had followed the river beyond the **territory** of friendly natives who knew them. They had entered a country of tribes made **hostile** and suspicious by the cruelties of Portuguese[2] slave traders.

"But see for yourselves," Livingstone had said to the group of unfriendly natives who had watched them making camp. "I am not like the Portuguese." He pointed to his straight hair and fair skin. "My God in the sky sent me to your country."

The natives, however, had remained suspicious. They could see that these strangers were of a different race than those

---

[1]Zambezi – zam bē′ zē

[2]Portuguese – pōr′ chə gēz

who kidnapped their people to sell as slaves across the big sea to the west. These white men had displayed no signs of **violence** toward the natives. But they trusted no strangers.

They saw the huge stack of boxes, tents, and equipment necessary for the long exploration into untracked territory of southern Africa. They saw the dozens of native porters who carried it. How did they know but what they contained weapons and the cruel chains and whips with which the Portuguese had herded defenseless Africans to the coast and to waiting slave ships? So, muttering and hostile, they had withdrawn to take counsel.

Livingstone retired to his tent to decide what to do next. The fate of the entire expedition rested upon his decision. He held in his hands the lives of his faithful followers, as well as the success of painful efforts to open up this dark continent for the Gospel.

In order to proceed with their journey, they must cross the mile-wide river which flowed into the Zambezi at this point. Should they attempt to get away under cover of darkness? Should they proceed or retreat? One thing Livingstone knew without a shadow of a doubt—God had called him to open up Africa to the Gospel and civilization. Nevertheless, he still needed God to show him when and how to do it.

"Lord," he prayed, "if I continue across the river against the wishes of these suspicious natives, they will pick us off like ducks with those poisoned arrows of theirs. Then who will bring the Gospel to this part of Africa? I will have caused the death of all my helpers, and the loss of all my supplies and equipment.

111

"But if I decide to turn back, all the time and money we have spent to get this far will be wasted. And the people who live beyond the river still may never hear the story of salvation. Lord, show me what to do."

The night hours passed and still he pondered. Finally he lighted a candle, and taking up his New Testament, opened it and read, "All power is given unto me in heaven and in earth. Go ye therefore, and teach all nations . . . . And, lo, I am with you alway, even unto the end of the world."

David Livingstone stood up, a look of peace on his face. "God has promised to be with those who obey His command. That settles it. I shall not cross furtively at night. Should a man with such a God flee? Nay, verily, I shall go even now and take observations for latitude and longitude. My God can handle these hostile men."

The next morning with the early summer sunrise, the explorers arose. David Livingstone gave orders to prepare to make the crossing. Hostile natives from all the surrounding country gathered silently to watch. Armed and threatening, they collected around Livingstone and his men, waiting for the next move. No native women or children appeared—a sure sign of intended violence.

Livingstone calmly went on with his preparations. The natives watched his every move.

The river was a mile broad at that point, and the explorers would be defenseless while making the crossing. The natives could afford to hold back until the explorers actually shoved off. Besides, it would take them several trips to ferry across all the goods, equipment, cattle, and men.

Then the natives began talking to each other. "Look at the White Chief. See that little round gold box full of wheels. Hear that clucking sound."

"That's why white men wear all those unnecessary clothes—to carry that funny little box."

"And all to tell time with!"

"Poh, doesn't the White Chief know how to tell time by the sun?"

"Look now! White Chief has a shiny stone, clear as water. You can see right through it."

"Poh! A fire! He made a fire with it! How could he do that?"

"He said he pulled down the heat from the sun. He knows something about the sun after all. Maybe he could teach us the magic of that clear stone that pulls fire from the sun."

The crowd had closed in around the missionary by now, **fascinated** by the strange possessions of this man who had come to their territory.

Livingstone showed his pen and his mechanical pencil. He unpacked all his personal things—scientific instruments, cooking utensils, books, clothing, anything that would hold their interest and curiosity. He showed how to use everything, allowing the savages to handle anything they desired.

Meanwhile, trip by trip, Livingstone's porters had been transporting the equipment and supplies across the broad river. The natives glanced that way occasionally, but made no move to prevent it.

At last only one canoe and its rowers remained. The missionary packed up the instruments and gadgets that had so fascinated the tribesmen. Now they saw that he carried no weapons or anything he could use to capture their people for slaves. He had made no hostile move toward them. The White Chief had told the truth. All the strange, wonderful things he carried showed that his God had indeed sent him from some far-off country.

Then the explorer offered a friendly hand to the head man of the group. "Thank you, Oh Chief, for your kindness," he said. "I wish you peace. Farewell." And with a wave to the crowd he climbed into the last canoe and shoved off.

Out on the broad river, David Livingstone stood up and waved to the group on the shore. Then he looked up into the blue African sky. "Thank you, my God, for Your great faithfulness."

And the natives on the shore whispered to each other. "Look, the White Chief talks to his God."

"For thou hast been a strength to the poor,
a strength to the needy in his distress."　　　　Isaiah 25:4

Invention From a Warm Heart

God could have answered Mother's faith with a load of
wood or a pile of coal. He might have gotten William a
good job or helped them find a warmer house. But He
answered her prayers in a way no one but God would have
thought of.

Beth took the basket that her brother William handed to
her upon entering the room. "Flour, tea, a little sugar, three
potatoes," Beth named the items as she arranged them on the
shelves in the kitchen.

"They did not give thee as much as sometimes," she said,
shivering a little. The small fire in the open fireplace did not
seem to warm the cold bare room at all. Even with her coat on
over her long gray woolen frock, she felt chilly.

"God will provide," said Mother. "If we pray and trust the
Lord, then someone will give wood or coal the next time," she
predicted cheerfully.

Outside, huge piles of snow bordered the low stone
doorsteps of the houses, and a chill wind blew up from the
wharves. In the street, men hurried along with heads bent

against the wind and their long cloaks wrapped closely around them.

The Arnold house felt almost as cold as the outdoors, for they had brought little with them to make life cheerful when they came across the sea to the new city of Philadelphia. And since Father had died, they had even less money than before. Mother earned some by sewing for other people, and William ran errands for the sailors down at the wharves. The sailors would put things in his basket in return for his work.

Now Mother coughed and clutched her shawl closer under her chin. Then she drew her chair up to the fireplace and got out her sewing. Beth watched her thin fingers trying to make the needle fly in and out of the white cloth.

"Thy fingers are stiff with the cold!" she exclaimed. She went to the fireplace and blew the coals into a flame with the **bellows.** Then she came and took her mother's hands in her own, and began rubbing the cold fingers.

"Not very stiff." Mrs. Arnold tried to smile.

"Yes, very," William said, as he swung his arms and blew on his own hands. "We could work easier if we didn't have to wear our coats to keep warm. And thy cough gets worse, Mother."

Just then they heard a rap at their door. Beth ran to open it, and both children shouted with delight as a familiar, slightly stooped figure entered. Long hair hung around the man's high forehead. Deep-set eyes shone kindly in his face. From his warm cloak he reached out to greet the family.

"Mr. Franklin!" Mother exclaimed. "Welcome. We are most

glad to see thee. Beth, make Mr. Franklin a cup of tea. Please excuse our small fire and cold house. Thee had better leave on thy cloak for a while."

"A small fire is better than none," remarked their guest. "Still I believe most of your heat is going up the chimney." The man glanced at Mother's shawl and the children's coats. When Mother coughed, he looked keenly at her, then said, "Mrs. Arnold, you should keep a bigger fire. You will never get rid of that cough in this cold room. Here, let me get it going better." He seized the bellows and began pumping vigorously. The flames **responded** immediately, dancing merrily up the chimney. "You should keep more coal on it," he said, setting the bellows aside.

"We cannot afford it," Mother replied. "God knows that, and He knows about my cough. He will provide what we need."

"Humph," grunted Mr. Franklin. Then he leaned over and peered up the chimney. He felt the bricks and measured with his eye the breadth and depth of the opening. "Hm, hm," he said thoughtfully.

Then his face broke into a pleased smile. "Hm, hm," he repeated in a satisfied tone.

"What does thee see up in our chimney?" asked Beth, as she handed the visitor a steaming cup of tea.

"A surprise," responded their neighbor, taking the cup. "A surprise."

"A surprise?" Beth looked puzzled. "How can thee see a surprise in the chimney?"

Mr. Franklin smiled. "Would it be a surprise if I told you? You will see after a while."

Then, instead of seating himself in the chair William pulled out, he drank the tea standing up and departed as quickly as he had come. But he left a warm glow of cheer behind him, for all Philadelphia enjoyed the friendliness of Benjamin Franklin.

"What did he mean?" Beth asked, after the door had closed behind their guest."

"I have no idea. But as busy as Mr. Franklin is, he'll forget about it by this time tomorrow," predicted William. He took out his speller and copybook and began to study, and the family soon forgot the words of their visitor.

Before long the little town of Philadelphia began to wonder at the doings at the big white house where Benjamin Franklin lived. The neighbors often heard sounds of hammering coming from the back where Mr. Franklin had built himself a work-shop. Now he set up a small **forge** to heat iron. Red-hot iron is soft and easy to work with. But why would Ben Franklin want to heat and shape iron?

Sailors unloaded great slabs of iron for him at the wharf and delivery men deposited them in his workshop. Then Mr. Franklin shut himself up, and from morning until night passers-by could see the flying sparks of the forge and hear the sound of its bellows. They heard ringing blows on iron coming from the shop as if it were the shop of a country black-smith. The neighbors all made predictions as to what the forge, the iron, and the hammering would produce, voicing their opinions to anyone who would listen. But no one ventured into the shop. None were courageous enough to inquire of Mr. Franklin himself.

Once in a while Mr. Franklin dropped in at the Arnold home

to bring a little gift of food and inquire after Mother's health. Each time he would check their fireplace and tell Mother she would never get rid of her cough and be able to work unless she kept the house warmer.

And every time, Mother replied, "The Lord knows that, and He will provide what we need."

Then Mr. Franklin would snort "Humph," and say nothing more.

"I don't think Mr. Franklin believes in God very much," said Beth, one day after their friend left.

"I know he does not believe," agreed Mother. "But he has a kind heart and God has used him to watch out for us since Father died. We must pray that he will come to believe the Word."

A few days after that God did, indeed, provide for the Arnolds. A friend of Mother's who lived on the other side of town invited the family to spend several weeks with her. When Mr. Franklin heard of it he offered to help them carry their bundles through the snowy streets to the friend's house. Mother took all her sewing jobs along.

As they set down their things inside the door of the big warm house, Beth could not keep from saying, "See, Mr. Franklin, God did provide for us. In this cozy place, Mother's cough will surely get better. Anyway, she will be able to get a lot of sewing done, because her hands will be warm."

But, as usual, Mr. Franklin only responded with "Humph." Then he smiled and said good-bye, promising to come help them carry their things home when they returned.

In her friend's big warm house, Mother's cough did slowly disappear. With plenty of good food she gradually regained her strength.

"Children, we must go home," she said one day. "I have sent word to Mr. Franklin. He will come this afternoon and help carry our bundles home. I have finished the sewing I brought along and now I must get home and find more work to do."

"But in that cold house thee will soon get sick again," predicted William. "I wish I had a better job so we could afford more coal."

"We will trust God, Son," admonished Mother quietly.

So they assembled their things and thanked Mother's friend for her kindness. Mr. Franklin arrived and they trekked homeward through the snowy streets. And all the while they noticed a sort of secret smile on their friend's kind face.

They understood the reason for that smile when they opened the door of their home.

"What...?"

"Oh!"

"How—why...?" They all stammered their surprise.

Had they come to the wrong house? No, there, just as they had left them, hung the row of shining copper pans on the wall. There stood the candlesticks on the mantelpiece. There sat the warming pan in the far corner, and there hung the bellows on its hook. The rag rugs lay before the fireplace as always.

But the room felt as warm as summer. Never had they enjoyed such comforting heat in the wintertime. The fireplace had not changed, but no fire burned there. All eyes riveted on a strange iron thing that squatted on the hearth. A fire burned in it, pouring warmth into the room. Instead of going up the chimney, the heat spread out until every corner felt warm.

Everyone turned to Mr. Franklin.

"What is it? Where did thee get it?"

A happy smile lighted their friend's eyes. "Did you forget I promised you a surprise? I invented this stove so all the heat will not go up the chimney. It will keep the coals alive all night, and not use as much fuel as the fireplace did."

The Arnolds could hardly wrench their eyes from Ben Franklin's wonderful invention. Nor could they find words to express their gratitude.

"See, children, I said that God would provide, but I never suspected anything like this." Mother struggled to keep her voice from quavering.

Then Mr. Franklin explained to William how the stove worked, and how to tend it. Beth bustled about the room, filling the teakettle and making a pot of tea.

Then she turned to their friend, her blue eyes looking deep into his. "Thee is so good to us. Why did thee work so hard to make this iron stove for us?"

Ben Franklin thought for a moment. Then he said, "Because the Arnold family has such warm hearts, I wanted them to have a warm house to live in."

"*Thee* has the warm heart," said Mother with tears in her voice. "God used thy warm heart to answer our prayers and provide for us, just as I told thee He would."

Mr. Franklin gave a snort and a grunt, but his warm smile embraced them all as he went out the door.

Many people today enjoy the warmth of a Franklin stove. The modern ones look much different and work better than the first one the inventor made. And we really do not know what gave Ben Franklin the idea for the stove or who he made it for. This story is how one person imagined it.

—Carolyn S. Bailey

Do you think this poem could describe the Arnolds' home?

My Home

There's laughter in the kitchen
And firelight on the hearth;
A warm house waits to greet me
If I come after dark.

Its walls are lined with comfort;   5
The door is open wide,
And I thank God in heaven
My loved ones wait inside.

When hearts are filled with caring
A home's a happy place;   10
Expressions of contentment
Are seen on every face.

—Elizabeth Hutto

*"For he commandeth, and raiseth the stormy wind,
which lifteth up the waves thereof."*   Psalm 107:25

Shipwreck!

*The Jews arrested the Apostle Paul and tried to kill him
because they hated his teaching about Jesus. This shipwreck occurred on the way to Rome where Paul would be
judged by Caesar, the Roman emperor. On the ship he had
a good bit of freedom, but was still a prisoner under the
guard of the Roman centurion (officer). The story, taken
from Acts 27 and 28, begins with their leaving Fair
Havens, even though Paul had warned the centurion that
they should not sail.*

27:13 And when the south wind blew softly, supposing that
they had obtained their purpose, loosing thence, they sailed
close by Crete.

14 But not long after there arose against it a **tempestuous**
wind, called Euroclydon[1]. 15 And when the ship was caught, and
could not bear up into the wind, we
let her drive. 16 And running under a
certain island which is called Clauda,
we had much work to come by the
boat: 17 Which when they had taken

> **verse 15:** They couldn't
> keep the ship facing the
> wind.

---

[1] Euroclydon (yü räk′ li dən) means "Northeast."

up, they used helps, undergirding the ship; and, fearing lest they should fall into the quicksands, strake sail, and so were driven.

> **verse 17:** They strengthened the ship by passing ropes under it.
>
> **verses 18, 19:** They threw out the cargo, plus ropes, pulleys, and things needed to sail the ship.

¹⁸ And we being exceedingly tossed with a tempest, the next day they lightened the ship; ¹⁹ And the third day we cast out with our own hands the tackling of the ship. ²⁰ And when neither sun nor stars in many days appeared, and no small tempest lay on us, all hope that we should be saved was then taken away.

²¹ But after long **abstinence** Paul stood forth in the midst of them, and said, Sirs, ye should have hearkened unto me, and not have loosed from Crete, and to have gained this harm and loss. ²² And now I exhort you to be of good cheer: for there shall be no loss of any man's life among you, but of the ship. ²³ For there stood by me this night the angel of God, whose I am, and whom I serve, ²⁴ Saying, Fear not, Paul; thou must be brought before Caesar: and, lo, God hath given thee all them that sail with thee. ²⁵ Wherefore, sirs, be of good cheer: for I believe God, that it shall be even as it was told me. ²⁶ Howbeit we must be cast upon a certain island.

²⁷ But when the fourteenth night was come, as we were driven up and down in Adria, about midnight the shipmen **deemed** that they drew near to some country; ²⁸ And sounded, and found it twenty fathoms²: and when they had gone a little further, they

> **verse 27:** They were driven about in the Adriatic Sea.
>
> **verse 28:** They dropped a weighted line into the water to find the depth.

²fathom – fa′ thəm: about six feet

125

sounded again, and found it fifteen fathoms. ²⁹ Then fearing lest we should have fallen upon rocks, they cast four **anchors** out of the stern³, and wished for the day.

³⁰ And as the shipmen were about to flee out of the ship, when they had let down the boat into the sea, under colour as though they would have cast anchors out of the foreship, ³¹ Paul said to the centurion and to the soldiers, Except these abide in the ship, ye cannot be saved. ³² Then the soldiers cut off the ropes of the boat, and let her fall off.

verse 30: Some tried to leave the ship in a boat, pretending they were dropping more anchors from the front of the ship.

³³ And while the day was coming on, Paul besought them all to take meat, saying, This day is the fourteenth day that ye have tarried and continued fasting, having taken nothing. ³⁴ Wherefore I pray you to take some meat: for this is for your health: for there shall not an hair fall from the head of any of you.

³⁵ And when he had thus spoken, he took bread, and gave thanks to God in presence of them all: and when he had broken it, he began to eat. ³⁶ Then were they all of good cheer, and they also took some meat. ³⁷ And we were in all in the ship two hundred threescore⁴ and sixteen souls. ³⁸ And when they had eaten enough, they lightened the ship, and cast out the wheat into the sea.

³⁹ And when it was day, they knew not the land: but they discovered a certain creek with a shore, into the which they were minded, if it were possible, to thrust in the ship. ⁴⁰ And

---

³stern – the back of the ship

⁴score – twenty

when they had taken up the anchors, they committed themselves unto the sea, and loosed the rudder bands, and hoisted
up the mainsail to the wind, and made toward shore. ⁴¹ And
falling into a place where two seas met, they ran the ship
aground; and the forepart stuck fast, and remained unmove-
able, but the hinder part was broken with the violence of the
waves.

⁴² And the soldiers' counsel was to kill the prisoners, lest
any of them should swim out, and escape. ⁴³ But the centurion, willing to save Paul, kept them from their purpose; and
commanded that they which could swim should cast themselves first into the sea, and get to land: ⁴⁴ And the rest, some
on boards, and some on broken pieces of the ship. And so it

came to pass, that they escaped all safe to land.

^{28:1} And when they were escaped, then they knew that the island was called Melita[5]. ² And the barbarous people showed us no little kindness: for they kindled a fire, and received us every one, because of the present rain, and because of the cold.

> **verse 2:** In Paul's day, anyone who did not speak Greek was considered a barbarian or uncivilized.

³ And when Paul had gathered a bundle of sticks, and laid them on the fire, there came a viper out of the heat, and fastened on his hand. ⁴ And when the barbarians saw the **venomous** beast hang on his hand, they said among themselves, No doubt this man is a murderer, whom, though he hath escaped the sea, yet vengeance suffereth not to live. ⁵ And he shook off the beast into the fire, and felt no

---

[5]Melita – mel′ i tə: an island in the Mediterranean, today called Malta.

harm. ⁶ Howbeit they looked when he should have swollen, or fallen down dead suddenly: but after they had looked a great while, and saw no harm come to him, they changed their minds, and said that he was a god.

⁷ In the same quarters were possessions of the chief man of the island, whose name was Publius; who received us, and lodged us three days courteously. ⁸ And it came to pass, that the father of Publius lay sick of a fever and of a bloody flux: to whom Paul entered in, and prayed, and laid his hands on him, and healed him. ⁹ So when this was done, others also, which had diseases in the island, came, and were healed: ¹⁰ Who also honoured us with many honours; and when we departed, they laded us with such things as were necessary.

—Acts 27:13—28:10

In the story of Paul's shipwreck, there was too much wind. The canoeist in this poem needed more wind; without it, she took down her sails and used her paddle instead.

The Song My Paddle Sings

West wind, blow from your prairie nest.
Blow from the mountains, blow from the west.
The sail is idle, the sailor too;
O wind of the west, we wait for you!

Blow, blow!   5
I have wooed you so,
But never a favor you bestow.
You rock your cradle the hills between,
But scorn to notice my white lateen.

I stow the sail and unship the mast: 10
I wooed you long, but my wooing's past;
My paddle will lull you into rest:
O drowsy wind of the drowsy west,
Sleep, sleep!
By your mountains steep,   15
Or down where the prairie grasses sweep,
Now fold in slumber your laggard wings,
For soft is the song my paddle sings.
 Be strong, O paddle! be brave, canoe!
 The reckless waves you must plunge into.   20

Reel, reel,
On your trembling keel,
But never a fear my craft will feel.

We've raced the rapids; we're far ahead:
The river slips through its silent bed.   25
Sway, sway,
As the bubbles spray
And fall in tinkling tunes away.

And up on the hills against the sky,
A fir tree rocking its lullaby   30
Swings, swings,
Its emerald wings,
Swelling the song that my paddle sings.

                                    —E. Pauline Johnson

Sometimes the wind is an enemy, as in the story of Paul's shipwreck. Sometimes it is a friend.

Wind and I

Wind,
You're loud.
You're keeping me awake.
You're whistling way off-key.
Why can't you be quiet?
Let me go to sleep.
You can sing in the morning.
Wind,
You're a pain!
But Wind—
I like you just the same!

Wind,
I'm tired of sitting here.
Why can't I go
Wherever I want, and
Whenever I want,
Like you?
I'm tired of sitting here.
Can't you take me with you?
Running off through the trees,
Feather-footing over the water,
Chasing the clouds in a game of tag?
Can't you?
I'm tired of sitting here.

Wind,
I'm coming!
I heard you calling me today,
And now I'm here
To play with you.
Now come!
Come toss my hair into my eyes!
Come blow my breath away!
And let's go running!
I'll race you, Wind—
Come on!

—Jennifer Crider

"He shall not be afraid of evil tidings: his heart is fixed, trusting in the LORD."

Psalm 112:7

In Spite of War

How could anyone go to sleep at night when war with its fighting and killing drew closer every day?

Lavina Rose Blosser watched the snow falling softly over the Valley of Virginia. It covered the countryside, a blanket of purity. Mother's garden stretched smooth and white down the hill to the barn. Snow softened and beautified the **stark** branches of the maple trees on the lawn. "It looks rested and peaceful," said the girl to herself, "not tired and on edge like I feel all the time these days."

"New Year's Day! And it's a beautiful morning! God has given the world a fresh start for 1863," Mother said softly, gazing at the peaceful countryside.

"If only men's hearts were as pure and clean as the snow." Father joined them at the window. "Then we would not have this fighting and bloodshed."

"Will we always have war, Father?" Amanda asked. She stood on tiptoe to peer out the window at the snow.

"We trust not, little one," Father said, lifting her into his arms.

"Do you think it's nearly over?" Lavina Rose asked hopefully. "I couldn't go to sleep for a long time last night worrying about things."

Father's face looked drawn and weary again. "No, Lavina Rose. It is not nearly over, but you must not worry. God is in control."

"Don't you think the Confederate[1] army is winning, Father?" Matthew asked eagerly. His voice had an **optimistic** ring. "I looked at the *Register* last evening, and I read about a battle they had at Fredericksburg just a couple of weeks ago. From that article it sounded like the South had such a big victory that the Union army would have to give up."

At sixteen, Matthew liked to keep up with the news. The little newspaper office in Harrisonburg had again started publishing the weekly *Register*.

"You mustn't believe everything you read, son," Father reminded him. "Yes, the Southern army won that particular battle. But on the whole, the South isn't in such good shape. The Confederate army hasn't nearly as many soldiers, nor as good a source for guns and ammunition. Remember, the North has most of the factories in their part of the country."

"That's why we can hardly get shoes and dress material and even farming supplies," Mother put in. "We always got those things from factories up in the North, and now the South is fighting the North."

No one spoke for a moment. Outside the window, they could see Danny, the terrier, **cavorting** in the snow. He danced circles around Stripey, as she picked her way daintily through

---

[1]Confederate – kən fed′ ər ət

135

the whiteness, her tail high in the air. Now and then she paused to stare disapprovingly at the frisky Danny. "You certainly do forget your **dignity**," she seemed to say, as her mouth opened in a silent meow.

They all laughed to see the animals. For a moment Lavina Rose felt relaxed and secure as she always had before the frightening Civil War had invaded the Shenandoah Valley.

Then Father grew serious again. "I do want you to be careful about reading the papers, Matthew," he cautioned. "You like to know what is going on, but you need to watch, or you'll find yourself taking sides and secretly wishing the South could kill more Northern soldiers so the South would win the war.

"The Southern newspapers naturally report good news about the Confederate army rather than the stark facts. They want to keep everyone keyed up and optimistic. A Northern paper would put quite a different slant on the same situation. In God's eyes both sides are equally wrong."

"And the papers play down the awful loss of lives," Mother added. "They praise the killing of thousands of enemy soldiers as a wonderful accomplishment. But each of those numbers stands for a person with a loving family, who likely is praying that their son or brother will come home safely. And even more serious, each one of them is a living soul who was hurled into eternity by someone else's hatred."

Lavina Rose wished they wouldn't talk about the war. In spite of what the newspapers said, she realized the Northern soldiers were drawing closer and closer.

"War scares me," Amanda said in a tight voice. "I can't go to sleep at night. What if the enemy soldiers come here?"

Amanda voiced Lavina Rose's own fears. The last two years had strained her nerves. Night was the worst. Her most **resourceful** attempts to fall asleep often failed. How could you go to sleep when disturbing pictures kept flooding into your mind—vague horrifying pictures of men killing one another? Every night she lay awake a long time, thinking and listening for the sound of guns. If only she could drop off to sleep as she used to before the war.

"Worship time, everyone," said Father cheerfully, changing the subject.

Matthew passed the hymnbooks around, and Lavina Rose pushed the disturbing thoughts to a back shelf of her mind as the comforting songs filled her heart.

Lessons followed family worship. Mother helped the children settle down with their slates and pencils, and Lavina Rose prepared to do sums. She thought wistfully of the little schoolhouse perched on the hill by Weaver's Church. Her older brothers had studied there the winters before the war. True, the teacher taught only a three-month term, but that was better than nothing. She hadn't been old enough to attend school before the war and now . . .

Lavina Rose sighed as she **mechanically** copied the first sum. They could not even use the schoolhouse now. Confederate soldiers often tied their horses around it and stored their belongings inside. They even used the meetinghouse for sleeping quarters sometimes—especially during the winter. For weeks the Mennonites had not used the building. Lavina Rose missed the quiet dignity of their Sunday church services. She missed meeting with the others to sing and pray and listen to their preachers. If only she could feel as carefree as the puppy cavorting in the snow around the old house cat. The pets had no worries about the war.

Lavina Rose watched Father and Matthew dressing to go outdoors to take care of the animals. Their boots looked sorry indeed, patched in every possible place by Mother's resourceful hands. "That's another thing we used to get from the North, I guess," she said to herself, noticing them.

Before going outside, Father paused to talk to Mother. He spoke in low tones so that he would not disturb the children's concentration on their lessons. Mother looked up from her bread dough to listen.

Lavina Rose kept her eyes on the sum on her slate, but her ears strained to hear Father's words.

"I want to get this week's paper if I can. Do you remember what President Lincoln said he would do on January 1?"

"Oh, that's right," Mother replied quietly as she folded and punched and turned her dough. "He said he would free the slaves if the South would not give up by January 1. I would be glad to see it."

"So would I," Father agreed. "Slavery always bothers me. People owning other *people* as if they were horses or cows! It certainly isn't right in God's sight. And I never could understand how a slave owner could live with his own conscience."

"Well, I must get to work." Father buttoned his coat and followed Matthew out into the snowy yard.

Lavina Rose's pencil mechanically kept working the sums. One corner of her brain, she added and carried and figured the answers to her math problems. The other part of her mind went to work on the problem of slavery.

On one side of their farm, just beyond the bridge, lived the Shenks. As Mennonites, of course, they did not own slaves. But if you walked around the hill on the west side of their farm, the Welles's acres came into view. In those fields you could often see black men hoeing or cultivating or cutting hay. Mr. Welles owned two slaves.

Mr. Welles treats his slaves well, Lavina Rose thought. *Gid and Joe always seem happy, singing or laughing. Mr. Welles usually works out in the field with them. He treats them more like hired men, only he doesn't pay them anything. And he could beat them or be really mean to them if he wanted to. But how sad they must be sometimes, since their families have been taken from them.*

Lavina Rose's thoughts rambled on while she neatly added a long column of figures, wrote a *3* and carried a *5. Mr. Welles gives them clothes and food and a shack to live in. But they could never leave unless they ran away. I don't believe any grown man would like that.*

Lavina Rose remembered several summers before the war when Gid had come to help them harvest their wheat. He had fascinated Lavina Rose with his wide grin and booming laugh. And how he could work! But hard work never brought Gid a cent of money. It never got him a better job like it did for a white man. No slave could do anything to change the fact that he was a slave.

"Mother, what would Gid and Joe do if the President freed the slaves? Where would they go?"

Mother turned around in surprise. "Did you hear what

Father said?" she asked. "I thought you were working at your lessons."

"Well, I was, but I listened too," Lavina Rose admitted.

"Free from what?" asked Amanda, laying down her pencil.

"Free from slavery. Free to come and go and do anything they please, just like we do. Now they belong to Mr. Welles—like, well, like his horses belong to him," Mother explained. "Mr. Welles bought them just like horses. He feeds them and gives them a place to sleep just like horses. They have to work just like horses at whatever he tells them to do. Maybe he treats them like he treats his horses. But he can whip them if they don't please him. And he could sell them at any time to others who might treat them cruelly.

"Gid and Joe can never leave the man who owns them. Nor will they ever get paid for the work they do," finished Mother.

"I would not like that," said Amanda seriously.

"Slaves don't like it either," said Mother, "but they can do nothing about it.

"Lavina Rose, if President Lincoln frees the slaves, things cannot change overnight. Slaveholding Southern farmers will not be able to farm such large farms without help, so they won't let them go unless the North wins the war and forces them to. Even if that happens, Gid and Joe and the other slaves will have a hard time of it. They can't read or write because it's against the law for a white man to teach them how. They don't have any money to get started in business. Even though they know how to farm, they don't own any land, so they will likely have a hard time providing for themselves.

"The most important thing is that they will be free. You and

I have no idea what that will mean to a slave."

"Slavery is terrible, isn't it, Mother?" asked Lavina Rose.

Mother oiled her hands and deftly shaped the bread dough into smooth round loaves. "Yes, it is. White men are no better or smarter than black men. God made all men of one blood. If Gid and Joe had the opportunities Mr. Welles has had, they could be as good a farmer or businessman as he. And they need salvation just like he does." Mother put the loaves of bread into the tin pans and covered them with a tea towel to rise.

"I remember Father talked to them about that," said Lavina Rose. "And Gid said, 'Well, that might be so for a white person like you, Mister Blosser, but I don't s'pose a black man has much chance with God.'"

"Poor Gid," said Mother. "God loves him just as much as He loves us; but you can hardly blame him for feeling that way. All his life white men have told him slaves are good for nothing but work. Some say they don't really have souls."

"I hope President Lincoln does free them, anyway," Lavina Rose stated. "Then the white people would have to pay them for their work. At least that would be a start."

"Yes, it would," agreed Mother. "Now children, you must get back to your work. God has all the affairs of our country in His hands, and we can trust everything to Him."

The kitchen became quiet again except for the scratch of slate pencils and the snap and crackle of the fire in the stove. Lavina Rose resolutely paid attention to her sums with one part of her mind. But with the other part she thought, *God has the Shenandoah Valley and the entire nation under His control!*

Neither the Union Army in the North nor the Confederate Army in the South is in charge of things. God is.

What a comforting thought! *I'm going to think about that tonight. Then I believe I can go to sleep right away.*

Blossers still live in the Shenandoah Valley of Virginia and attend Weavers Mennonite Church, although it is a different building than the one Confederate soldiers took over in the story.

God has blessed the Shenandoah Valley with peace and prosperity. For many years, children there have not needed to lie awake at night pondering on slavery or worrying about war coming to their area.

—Joyce Miller

Could you obey these commands and fight in a war or own slaves at the same time?

Love Your Enemies

But I say unto you which hear,
   Love your enemies,
      do good to them which hate you,
   Bless them that curse you, and
      pray for them which despitefully use you.

And unto him that smiteth thee on the one cheek
      offer also the other;
and him that taketh away thy cloke
      forbid not to take thy coat also.
Give to every man that asketh of thee;
      and of him that taketh away thy goods
        ask them not again.

And as ye would that men should do to you,
   do ye also to them likewise.

                 –Luke 6:27-31

The Blosser family, like this poet, enjoyed seeing a world full of snow.

The Snow

See the snow!
Falling slow—
Out of the gray cloud stooping low,
So airy light,
So pure and white,
Like quiet showers
Of sky-garden flowers,
Silently, softly sinking down,
Wreathing the branches bare and brown,
Robing the roofs of the busy town.

Soft and fair
Through the white air,
Here and there and everywhere.
Falling slow, in a quiet so deep
That all the world seems going to sleep.
But here comes the breeze,
Sounding his fife through the snowbound trees—
See them bow and bend and sway.
He lifts the boughs, and dances away
Through the flying mist of the crystal spray.

He crosses
The line of falling flakes, and tosses
The airy white mosses
Hither and thither,
Who knows whither?
Up and down; all through town; low and high—
Straight into the face of the passerby;
Blowing each flake like a flying feather,
Twirling them, whirling them all together
In a hurry and flurry of wintertime weather.

Look aloft!
How fine! how soft!
See the down-feathers ceaselessly waft.
How graceful, how fair
They dance in the air;
Now fast, now slow.
And so comes the snow—
In a lazy motion, drifting below.
Out of the gray clouds stooping low—
Come the graceful white petals of beautiful snow.

"The God in whose hand thy breath is, and whose are all thy ways, hast thou not glorified." Daniel 5:23

Ship Unsinkable

Have you ever noticed how often a person fails to do the thing he brags about doing? The Bible says God resists the proud. Could that be the reason?

Imagine standing on a street corner in a city. Four blocks away you see someone waving. Is he waving at you? Can you tell who it is?

Now picture a ship four blocks long—as long as from where you stand to that person waving at you.

Look at the building beside you. Look up, up, up. Eleven floors up. Can you imagine a ship that tall? Four blocks long and eleven stories high! No wonder they named it *Titanic.* Titan[1] was the name of a mythical race of giants.

1912. In those days before airplanes, thousands of people crossed the Atlantic Ocean between Europe and America every year. People from Europe wanted to **emigrate** from their home-lands and settle in the United States. Rich businessmen traveled back and forth because America and Europe sold and bought products from each other. Everyone had to travel by ship.

---

[1]Titan – tī′ tən

Shipping companies made a lot of money transporting people and goods across the Atlantic. The bigger the ship, the more it could carry. The faster it traveled, the better the passengers liked it, and the sooner it could return for another load. Naturally shipping companies wanted big, fast ships.

In 1907, more than 1,200,000 **immigrants** had arrived in the United States. And still they kept coming. That year the Cunard Steamship Line **launched** two new ocean liners. Because they were the fastest ships afloat, they became the most popular vessels on which to cross the ocean.

Then the owners of a **rival** company, the White Star Line, began to dream. They dreamed of two new ships of their own. They dreamed and began to plan for two ships bigger and better than those of their rivals.

In 1911, their dream came true. The White Star Line launched two new ships. Both had been built in Europe. The first one, named *Olympic,* began its maiden voyage on May 31 of that year. But its sister ship, the *Titanic,* still needed some months to be finished on the inside and outfitted for travel.

The *Olympic* and *Titanic* could not travel quite as fast as the two ships of the Cunard Line. But both were larger and much finer. In fact, the *Titanic* was the largest moving man-made thing in the world. Moreover, no other ocean liner on earth could boast as beautiful and **luxurious accommodations.**

Those luxurious accommodations included plush carpets, carved woodwork, a dining room that seated 500 people, a swimming pool, dance hall, game rooms, and lounges. A band provided music for any occasion, and hundreds of servants were ready to make the beds, serve the meals, shine the shoes, and clean the rooms of the rich, first-class passengers.

For these luxuries rich people paid $4350 for a first-class ticket on the maiden voyage of the *Titanic*. That would amount to around $50,000 in our money today.

Second-class passengers paid what would amount to $750 nowadays. People who bought a third-class, or steerage, ticket paid $35 in 1912, a value of about $400 today.

Steerage was located in the bottom of the ship. That was where cattle were penned when being transported from America to Europe. On the way back from Europe these ships would load up with poor emigrants who wanted to begin a new life in America. Those people could not afford better accommodations, so they had to travel in steerage, which was crowded, dirty, and smelly.

But not on the *Titanic*. This was her maiden voyage and even steerage was spotless.

In the lowest part of the ship, you would also find the "greasers," the men who shoveled coal into the ship's monstrous furnaces. The *Titanic* burned 650 tons of coal a day to fire the gigantic boilers that produced the steam. The steam turned the three huge propellers that drove the floating palace through the water.

A ship that weighs thousands upon thousands of tons cannot move like a speedboat on a lake. And a ship's speed is not measured by miles per hour. Rather, we say a ship travels at so many knots. A knot is somewhat longer than a mile. The *Titanic* held a good speed at 21 knots. Even modern ships of today do not travel much faster than that.

White Star owners had named this gigantic ship the *RMS*

Titanic. Those initials stood for "Royal Mail Ship." Nearly 3500 bags of mail had been stashed in the hold, along with 900 tons of baggage.

Not only did the *Titanic*'s builders want her to be the most beautiful and luxurious ship, but they also intended that she be the safest. Too many ships had sunk because they began leaking or had broken apart in a storm.

So they constructed the *Titanic* with a double hull, two layers of steel, one inside the other. Other ships had only one layer of steel on the sides and bottom. Not only that, they built sixteen watertight compartments into the lower part of the ship. Even if some of them filled with water, the others would keep the great ship afloat.

In obedience to the law, the *Titanic* carried lifeboats—20 of them. The law required them to carry 16 if the ship weighed over 10,000 tons. Also according to law, they carried eight white rockets. When shot from the ship, and exploded in the sky, they were the universal signal of a ship in trouble.

Two wireless operators manned the wireless room, ready to send messages to other ships. They also received radiograms which informed the passengers of events happening on land.

Partway up the foremost mast hung the crow's nest. This bucket-like affair held two lookouts who constantly scanned the ocean for anything that could cause trouble.

The White Star Line advertised the *RMS Titanic* as unsinkable. One official is said to have declared, "Even God couldn't sink this ship."

The *Titanic*'s captain, Edward J. Smith, had sailed the oceans for 38 years. What an honor to captain the world's largest and safest ship! After this maiden voyage of the unsinkable *Titanic,* he planned to retire and sail no more.

Hundreds of rich and well-known people in Europe wanted to travel to America on the new ship. Hundreds of emigrants from different European countries had booked passage on her.

On April 10, over 2,200 passengers boarded the *Titanic.* Hundreds of relatives and friends and sightseers stood on the dock waving good-bye as the great ship moved majestically away from her moorings.

Now listen to an imaginary conversation between the two lookouts in the crow's nest late Sunday night, April 14, 1912.

FRED: Mighty cold up here tonight.

REGINALD: Just be glad the wind isn't blowing. I don't think I ever saw the ocean so calm and still.

FRED: Yes, it sure is quiet. Guess everyone's gone to bed. Nothing else to do since they won't allow dancing on Sunday.

REGINALD: That's what I like about Sunday on Captain Smith's ship. Church and a hymn-sing like we had today.

FRED: Yes, I like that too, but those warnings off and on all day about icebergs in the vicinity make me nervous. 'Course we didn't see a sign of an iceberg all day. Maybe that's why the Captain didn't pay any attention when the wireless operators kept repeating those warnings to him.

But it's dark now, and no moon. We're the ones responsible for spotting icebergs, and they didn't even give us binoculars. If I were captain, I'd slow this ship down with icebergs around.

REGINALD: I'm afraid the Captain wants to impress all the high-class passengers on board. We have one of the richest men in the world right down there below us. And you know, the director of the White Star Line who owns this ship came along too.

FRED: I heard that. And I heard that he encouraged Captain Smith to speed up—that maybe we could make it to New York by Tuesday evening rather than Wednesday morning."

REGINALD: That would make the White Star Line look good sure enough—crossing the Atlantic in six days instead of seven.

FRED: We won't get there at all if we hit an iceberg. Wish we had binoculars. Who can see anything when it's this dark?

REGINALD: I know, but stop your worrying. You're forgetting that this ship is unsinkable.

FRED: Well, it's after eleven thirty. Our watch is about over and we'll be out of this freezing crow's nest and down in our warm cabin. Let the next watch worry about icebergs.

REGINALD: Fred! Look! In front there! What's that big gray thing?

FRED: Captain Smith! Captain Smith! Lookout reporting iceberg dead ahead!

Almost, *almost,* the slowly veering *Titanic* missed the looming mountain of ice in its path. The bow with the petrified lookouts slid past. Then far below the waterline—bump—bump—bump—bump—bump—bump. Then the giant vessel moved on into the night. Sleeping passengers slept on. Those still awake felt a slight shudder, "as though we went over about a thousand marbles," one said.

Only the crew knew the *Titanic* had been wounded. The

151

iceberg had buckled the steel hull, letting water through six small gashes into six of the compartments.

Captain Smith took one look at the Atlantic Ocean roaring into the hull.

"Signal for help! Fire the rockets! Lower the lifeboats!" Even as he bellowed these orders, the Captain realized one horrifying fact. The beautiful ship that nothing could sink had become in one minute the ship that nothing could keep afloat!

For all the money and forethought her builders had spent to make the *Titanic* safe, she lacked three things that night. Three things that someone considered unimportant.

One was binoculars in the crow's nest. With binoculars, the lookouts could have spotted the iceberg in plenty of time to avoid a collision.

A second lack was a lifeboat drill. Captain Smith had not ordered a lifeboat drill the first day out, as was standard procedure for a ship. With so many rich society people aboard, perhaps he didn't want to bother them with something as inelegant as a lifeboat drill. They wouldn't need it anyway on an unsinkable ship.

So the crew had not practiced lowering the lifeboats on the new ship. They did not know how to handle frightened people and fill the lifeboats in a speedy and efficient way. The passengers had no idea how to board the boats, nor had they been assigned to any particular boat. Consequently, many lifeboats that could have held sixty people pulled away with only half as many passengers as they could have carried.

The third most tragic lack of all was too few lifeboats. The

Titanic complied with the law requiring 16 lifeboats for ships weighing over 10,000 tons. However, she weighed more than four times that much, and needed nearly four times as many boats to accommodate the total number of people she could carry. On this maiden voyage, there was lifeboat space for only half the people on board.

Lifeboats hung above deck between two upright poles called davits. When needed, the davits swung the boats out over the rail and then lowered them by ropes and pulleys level with the deck. After the people stepped from the deck into one of the boats, it was lowered to the water.

On this maiden voyage of the *Titanic* with so many distinguished people aboard, the owners did not want to clutter the upper deck with the necessary number of lifeboats. So even if

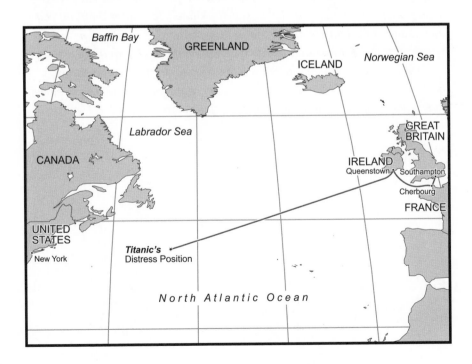

all the lifeboats had been filled to capacity, a thousand passengers still would have had no way to escape the sinking ship.

For the *Titanic* was sinking. During the two hours since she had swiped the iceberg, her bow had been sinking lower and lower. Her stern rose higher and higher in the darkness. Lower and lower and lower. Then, almost gently, she slid out of sight.

Down, through the cold waters of an unexplored ocean. Down, down, past sea creatures which fled from the monstrous alien form. Down, down, down, more than two miles where daylight never reaches, the unsinkable *Titanic* settled into the mud of the North Atlantic Ocean.

More than 1,500 people went down with the great ship, including Captain Smith. Only 705 survived to be picked up by a rescue ship several hours later. The sinking of the Titanic *shocked the world and led to new safety rules for all ships. In 1985, seventy-three years after the fatal voyage, a team of scientists discovered and explored the wreckage of the* Titanic, *taking pictures and learning more about the ship and the disaster.*

One story cannot begin to tell the whole story of the Titanic. *Many books have been written about the disaster in the nearly 100 years since that night. You can find some of them in your library.*

−Ruth K. Hobbs

The makers of the Titanic *thought that bigger was better. But when the Titanic met up with an iceberg, they realized that bigger just sank faster.*

What happens when a kayak meets an iceberg? Read this poem to find out.

The Kayak

Over the briny wave I go,
In spite of the weather, in spite of the snow;
What cares the hardy Eskimo?
In my little skiff, with paddle and lance,
I glide where the foaming billows dance.   5
Round me the birds slip and soar;
Like me, they love the ocean's roar.
Sometimes a floating iceberg gleams
Above me with its melting streams;
Sometimes a rushing wave will fall   10
Down on my skiff and cover it all.
But what care I for a wave's attack?
With my paddle I right my little kayak,
And then its weight I speedily trim,
And over the water away I skim.   15

–Author Unknown

"Give to every man that asketh of thee; and of him that taketh away thy goods ask them not again."   Luke 6:30

Home on His Own

Lennie didn't want the bishop to disobey the Bible. At the same time, he didn't want him to lose his most valuable horse. Why did his employer set up such an impossible condition for taking the horse back?

Every Thursday Lennie jogged across the back pasture to Bishop Benedict Miller's farm to help there for the day. Before going to the house, Lennie always swung around by the barn to spend a few minutes with Samson. The first stall inside the door belonged to the big dapple-gray Percheron, which Lennie had spoiled with carrots and apples.

The boy always gave his special whistle when he entered the barnyard. He could count on hearing an answering whinny and seeing Samson's great gray head stretching over the half-door by the time he entered.

In those days of the early 1880s, long before tractors, no one could farm without **adequate** horsepower in the form of living horses. Benedict Miller owned many horses, but none so strong, so gentle, or so valuable as the big Percheron.

This morning Lennie gave his special whistle, but when he

entered the barn, no huge friendly horse greeted him. The boy leaned over the Dutch door and gave one **perplexed** glance around the empty stall, then ran for the house.

"Where's Samson?" He blurted out the question the instant the door opened.

"Samson?" repeated the bishop in a puzzled tone. "In his stall as far as I know."

"But he isn't!" cried Lennie.

The bishop grabbed his hat and the two hurried from the house. "He's probably loose in the barn somewhere," surmised the bishop. "I sometimes neglect to hook his stall door. But I know I latched the barn door, so he couldn't have gotten out."

"Yes, it was latched," **verified** Lennie, "and so was Samson's stall."

"Hmmm, that's funny," murmured the man a minute later as he looked into the deserted stall and examined the hook on the door. "I have known Samson to unhook his door a time or two. But he isn't smart enough to close the door and fasten it after himself. That I know. Only a human could do that."

A dark suspicion sprang up in Lennie's mind. "You don't suppose . . ." he ventured.

"Definitely a possibility." The bishop's **rejoinder** told Lennie that they both feared the same thing. "Let's look around. The back lane first."

The man and boy set off examining the soft earth of the grassy lane. They had not gone far before Lennie cried, "Look here! Samson's tracks! He came out this lane not too long ago!"

"And see this," Benedict pointed out a little farther on, "a man's shoe print."

"Here's another one," exclaimed Lennie, his voice shrill with excitement, as he hurried on ahead of the bishop.

"And look at this. Here Samson's track half covers the shoe track. That shows he was following the man, or rather, that the man was leading him. Someone's stolen him!"

"So I fear. So I fear," remarked the bishop. "The man certainly made no effort to hide his tracks, did he?"

"No. We can follow him easily. Let's hurry. Maybe we can catch him."

Lennie ran on, spotting Samson's big hoof prints now and again along the grassy lane. Finally the lane came out onto a dusty country road. The boy stopped and waited for the farmer.

When the bishop came up, he gazed at the road stretching emptily in both directions. "Well, I guess that's that," he said with a sigh.

"Oh, no," protested Lennie, bending over to **scrutinize** the dust of the road. "They went this way. Look here."

Sure enough they could see where Samson's big hoofs had gone splat, splat in the thick dust of the road toward the mountain.

"We can follow them. They can't have gotten far away."

"Never mind, never mind, my boy," said the bishop. "He's off my land. I'll pursue him no farther. Let him go."

"Let him go!" shrilled Lennie. "Not Samson! Why Samson's your best horse!"

"I know. I know. And my favorite, too. We don't always understand the ways of the Lord, do we, Lennie?" Bishop Benedict spoke in a voice of patient sorrow.

The farmer's words shocked and frightened Lennie with their finality. Samson gone for good? Never again to stroke that long gray face and velvety muzzle? Until that moment Lennie hadn't known how much he loved the big dapple Percheron. Now he realized Samson was the reason why he always looked forward to Thursdays.

"But, Brother Benedict, you shouldn't let the thief get away with this. He'll keep on stealing. He'll come back and steal some of your other horses if he knows you won't do anything."

"Maybe so, maybe so." The bishop nodded his head in agreement, but made no further remark. He turned to go back to the farm.

Lennie felt desperate. "Don't you care? Don't you *want* Samson back?" he cried almost in tears.

"Yes, yes, Lennie. Of course I want Samson back. But more than that, I want to do what God has commanded. 'The Lord gave, the Lord hath taken away.' After all, he really is God's horse, you know. Everything I own belongs to God."

"But couldn't you at least let people know someone stole him? You can't hide a horse as big as Samson. Someone will surely see him and let you know, then you can go and bring him back."

"No, no. I won't go after him or try to find him. Let him come home on his own. God can send him back if He wants me to have him."

Lennie said nothing more as they walked back to the farm. He said little as he worked the rest of the day. He felt like he had just come from a funeral. He could hardly endure the thought that Samson was getting farther and farther from home while no one did anything to prevent it.

A seed of anger and bewilderment began growing in his heart. He knew, he just *knew* that God would not command you to let a thief walk away with your best horse and not try to get him back.

At home that evening he poured out the whole story to his parents.

"That's a real loss," Papa remarked soberly.

"And just at plowing time, too," Mama added. "He'll be handicapped without his best horse. Isn't there a chance of getting him back? The thief can't have gotten far."

"That's what I said," Lennie replied. "But Brother Benedict's not going to try to find him. He said God commands us not to. He said Samson belongs to God, and He can do anything He pleases with His own property."

"That sounds like Brother Benedict," murmured Mama.

"He's right though. There *is* Scripture that says we shouldn't ask a thief to give back what he stole. I think it's in the Sermon on the Mount. Let me see if I can find it." Papa picked up his Bible from the shelf.

A few minutes later Lennie listened in astonishment as Papa read, " 'Give to every man that asketh of thee; and of him that taketh away thy goods ask them not again.' That's Luke 6:30."

So the Bible *did* say that—just as plain as it could be. Now Lennie understood why Brother Benedict would make no effort to **retrieve** Samson from the thief.

Gradually the boy's anger and bewilderment evaporated.

Instead, admiration for his employer filled his heart. Benedict Miller had promptly and cheerfully obeyed the Lord in spite of the financial loss, in spite of the setback in his farm work, in spite of his affection for Samson. He obeyed, knowing he would never see his big gentle horse again. What a good brave man!

In no time it seemed all Somerset County heard how a horse thief had robbed an Amish bishop of a valuable Percheron. And they heard that the bishop had refused to follow the robber, even though he could easily have caught him. How tongues flapped over the story.

Many people became angry that the bishop had let the man escape. In those days everyone despised a horse thief, for without a horse, a man had no means of transportation. Without a horse, a farmer could not make a living.

When Papa returned from town, he reported other reactions to the situation. "A lot of people respect Brother Benedict for sticking to what he believes, but they think he holds to a queer notion of what is right and wrong. Others feel sorry for him because his religion makes him lose a valuable horse."

"He's not queer," exclaimed Lennie indignantly. "He did what the Bible says, so he's right. No one needs to feel sorry for him. But Papa, don't you think God will probably send Samson back somehow, since Brother Benedict obeyed Him?"

"No, Lennie, we obey God because we love Him and want to please Him, not in hopes of getting something we'd like to have. I can think of no way that Samson could come back on his own, like the bishop has specified. Can you?"

"No, I guess not," admitted Lennie reluctantly. "Even if

Samson escaped from the thief, someone else would catch and keep him. Or if he brought him back, the bishop wouldn't take him, anyway. He says Samson must return on his own."

The next Thursday while Lennie worked in the barn with Brother Benedict, a group of non-Christian neighbors arrived. The bishop stepped outside to meet them, but Lennie could not help hearing the conversation.

"We'll go after that thief for you. We'll get your big horse back, and you won't have to do a thing."

"No, no, my friends," protested the bishop emphatically. "I thank you kindly. But God has given His instructions on the matter, and I will follow them. I cannot consent to your doing any such thing for me."

"You don't have to consent. We men will run down that thief and punish him as he deserves. We'll put Samson back in his stall as a favor to a good neighbor," stated one of the group.

"I will not accept the horse unless he returns all by himself. Then I will know God wants me to have him back," said Brother Benedict with quiet finality. He turned away, and the men knew they could do nothing more to help their friend retrieve his stolen property.

"The bishop didn't budge an inch," reported Lennie in admiration at the supper table.

"Couldn't you have guessed that?" asked Papa.

"Yes, but wouldn't it be all right to let those other men go after Samson? That's different than doing it himself, isn't it?"

"So you think he should let others do what the Bible forbids in order to get his horse back?"

"Oh." Lennie could say nothing more. Now he understood why the farmer insisted that the horse would have to return on his own.

Several months passed. Talk died down about the stolen work horse in Somerset County. Bishop Benedict cheerfully continued his busy schedule of farming and preaching.

And Lennie continued to jog across the back pasture on Thursdays to help him. But he never passed Samson's empty stall without remembering the big gentle Percheron and wondering where he was and if he had been sold to a good master.

He dreamed splendid dreams of finding Samson and leading him in triumph home to the bishop. But at that point his dream always collapsed because he knew his employer would not take the horse back because he had not returned on his own.

"You'd never guess what I heard in town today," announced Papa one evening the minute he entered the house. "Neighbor John saw a huge dapple-gray Percheron fastened to a hitching rack in Baltimore."

"In Baltimore," echoed Mama. "That's ninety miles away! It couldn't be Samson, could it?"

"John thought it was. Anyway, he waited until the owner showed up, and asked him about it. The man said he had bought the horse from a stranger rather recently. When John told him he probably had bought a stolen horse, the man said he'd sell him if the owner could prove it belonged to him."

"Now what?" asked Mama. "Brother Benedict won't go to Baltimore to identify the horse."

"You are right. He's already told us that," said Papa. "But the neighbors and I have concocted a plan."

"What kind of plan?"

Papa smiled a satisfied smile. "John is convinced the horse is Samson, so all of us are going to chip in and buy him and bring him home."

"But what if it isn't Samson? All Percherons look about alike to me. And if the bishop won't have anything to do with getting him back, he won't consent to identify him."

"I'll know right away if it's Samson. He'll recognize me!" Lennie cried excitedly.

"Yes, Lennie, we're counting on you to give us proof of that. Then we'll turn him loose and see where he goes."

One day sometime later, a mile from the bishop's farm, Lennie and Papa waited beside the dusty road. It seemed the whole neighborhood had congregated with them. They peered down the road, until around the bend came two men leading a huge dapple-gray Percheron. Was it Samson, or wasn't it?

As they drew nearer, Lennie, according to instructions, hid behind the group of excited men and boys. Then loud and shrill he gave his special whistle.

Up went the big head. The ears pricked forward, as with an eager whinny the horse quickened his pace. With a handful of carrots, Lennie wormed his way through the crowd and ran toward his friend.

"It *is* Samson! It *is* Samson!" shouted a dozen voices. And no one doubted that they shouted the truth.

"Now stand back, folks," instructed Papa. "Lennie, get out of sight."

The crowd drew back. Papa turned the big animal so that he faced away from the bishop's farm. Then he unclipped the lead rope from the halter and stepped aside.

Now a dead silence descended on the group. Lennie held his breath. Would Samson remember the way home?

For a minute the great horse just stood there as if thinking. He looked from side to side. He shook his head and snorted. Then slowly he wheeled completely around and began walking. The people fell in behind.

"Don't get too close," cautioned Lennie, "or the bishop will say we chased him home. And be quiet or we'll distract him."

What a strange procession. A huge dappled gray horse followed by a crowd of whispering men and boys.

At the intersection where Benedict's lane came out onto the main road, Samson turned in without hesitation. Now he began walking faster.

"Well, men," spoke up Neighbor John. "We did it. I guess this is where we stop. We can't let the bishop see us. But Lennie, maybe you'd better circle ahead to see how it all turns out."

The boy needed no urging. He took off like a streak.

So from behind a shed, only Lennie saw Samson come pacing majestically up the back lane. Only Lennie saw the horse break into a trot as he neared the barn. Only Lennie saw him turn and swing into the first stall inside the barn door.

And no one but Lennie saw the look on Bishop Benedict's face when he glanced up from his work nearby and saw his favorite horse coming home, truly on his own.

The basic events of this story are true. Bishop Benedict Miller was a real person. He owned a Percheron who was stolen and came home on his own as described here. The tale has been told many times over the last hundred years.

However, in this version of the story, Samson is an imaginary name. Lennie is imaginary. The other characters and what they said and did are largely imaginary. The writer supplied all those details to bring you the true account of how God rewarded the loving obedience of one of His children.

– Mary Clemens Meyer

OUT IN NATURE

Open Range

Prairie goes to the mountain,
    Mountain goes to the sky.
The sky sweeps across to the distant hills
And here, in the middle,
    Am I.

Hills crowd down to the river,
    River runs by the tree.
Tree throws its shadow on sun-burnt grass
And here, in the shadow,
    Is me.

Shadows creep up the mountain,
    Mountain goes black on the sky,
The sky bursts out with a million stars
And here, by the campfire,
    Am I.

–Kathryn & Byron Jackson

*"**W**here is the dwelling of the lions, and the feedingplace of the young lions, where the lion, even the old lion, walked?"*

Nahum 2:11

Lions in the Night

Hunters who go to Africa to hunt big game need courage and skill in order to bag any wild animals. But getting a close-up shot with a camera requires much more work, skill, and courage than pulling a trigger at a distance. People around the world still enjoy the photographs taken by Martin and Osa Johnston.

I am Dick Douglas and this is a true story of one of the African adventures David Martin, Douglas Oliver, and I had in the summer of 1928. We were spending the summer with those great photographers of big game, Martin and Osa Johnston. One day we planned to get pictures of lions. Mr. Johnston set up the cameras in the afternoon and placed the kill. The kill was a zebra **carcass** that served as lion bait. The rest of us stayed in camp.

About sunset we all drove to the spot where Mr. Johnston had set the kill, then positioned the vehicles so that their backs faced the zebra carcass. Martin and Osa camped at the edge of a ditch with the plains behind them. We parked between two ditches and within shouting distance of the Johnstons. The back of our covered truck faced the dead zebra, with the cameras in between. Wires ran from the cameras into the back of the truck where we boys planned to sleep. We also were supposed to take pictures of any lions that came.

Heavy wire formed the sides of our truck. As it had a good top, we only had to close the front and back. To make these safe we lashed poles across both openings. After we got into the back of the truck, we wired poles across the front. This **partition** shut off the front seat from the bed of the truck.

We felt sure the lions could not get to us, yet we all felt a little nervous when Mr. Johnston left. We got ready for bed while we could still see, then ate the lunch that Mrs. Johnston had prepared for us.

Someone had told us that if lions heard a human voice they would instantly run. It was likely, though, that even if the animals were not afraid, we would have whispered because we were all so excited.

Just as we started to eat, Dave whispered something about this being our last meal on earth. We all laughed; but little remarks like that, at such a time, make one feel somewhat uncomfortable. To be sure, we had agreed to fire the rifle twice if we needed Mr. Johnston; however, what good would that do since our friends would be a considerable distance away and the lions only a few feet?

About half an hour after we had crawled under the blankets, we suddenly heard a bone crack. We slowly rose and positioned ourselves shoulder to shoulder at the back of the truck. Then we shone the flashlight out between the poles and strained our eyes toward the kill. We saw a huge old male lion with a short mane. He did not run away, but only crouched down behind the carcass and lashed his tail from side to side. When we saw him, we all started shaking, not so much in fright as from excitement at seeing a lion just a few feet away.

As we watched, he got over his nervousness and started eating on the zebra. We could hear him plainly as he tore out great chunks of meat and devoured them. Now and then he snarled and growled deeply in his throat. For several minutes we watched him.

Then Dave whispered, "Let's try for a picture." So we started whistling to make him hold up his head. When we first whistled, he ran off a few feet but soon returned. We whistled again and he only looked up at us. Now Dave caught hold of the two wires that controlled the flares. To set them off, he had to touch the two wires together. The lion looked up just then, but didn't seem to be in the right position. Dave was going to whistle once more, but just as he drew in his breath, the camera flare went off with a loud bang and blinding flash. His hands had been shaking so much that the wires had touched without his intending it.

At the flash, the lion ran off, **blundering** through the bushes because the light blinded him. "I don't think he was even in the picture," Dave lamented.

Doug answered, "I expect Mr. and Mrs. Johnston think we are crazy, taking a picture at this time of night."

"Well," I said. "It was certainly a relief to see that lion vamoose."

170

In a few minutes we heard Mr. Johnston calling. Doug whispered, "They're probably laughing at us and saying, 'Those boys most likely photographed a hyena, mistaking it for a lion.'"

Mr. Johnston called, "What did you get?"

"Only a lion," we answered carelessly.

"Well, go to sleep," he yelled back. "We'll see in the morning."

This was about eight o'clock, so we crawled under our blankets, expecting no more excitement that night. We remained awake for half an hour, then dropped off to sleep.

Several hours later, a violent shaking of the truck wakened us. We heard growling outside. After some minutes of lying in bed, shivering with both fright and excitement, we got up enough courage to shine our lights out the back. Just under us stood an old lioness calmly chewing on a tire! Twenty-five feet away, on the kill, crouched four other lions. As we watched, two more joined them. Then the old lioness padded back to the group. We counted three big males with manes, three females, and one *toto,* or young one.

We believe it was the most exciting moment of our lives, besides being one of the most interesting.

In spite of their fierce looks, the lions acted exactly like a bunch of cats quarreling over a meal. They lay there, one at the head of the zebra, two at the back, two at the side, and one on the haunches. The *toto* stood off a few feet, watching his chance to venture into the feast. Our light seemed not to bother them, for they only looked up now and then and blinked. However, the male whose picture we had taken seemed a bit uneasy. At first when we moved the light, he would crouch down behind the carcass. Eventually, he got over his nervousness.

After a while the *toto* crawled up beside one of the big fellows. So long as he kept to his place, they allowed him to eat. But once when he got up too close and started for the same bit of meat as one of the others, the big male rose up and lashed out at him. It seemed a light blow, but it sent the *toto* rolling into the grass. He jumped up and ran over to the other side of the carcass where he squatted down beside a lioness, probably his mother.

We almost laughed aloud. The scene might well have been that of a human family at a meal. We were witnessing the way the lion usually behaves. He spends his whole life in search of food—killing, eating, and sleeping. We were seeing what happens every night of his life.

They seemed tame and playful enough, but when we heard their growls and deep rumblings as they gulped down large chunks of meat, we could not think of them as anything other than lions, rulers of the plains and forests.

After we had watched them for some time by the light of our flashlights, we noticed that they had knocked down one of the cameras. As we whispered about this, one of the big lions left the kill, walked over to the fallen camera, and began chewing on it. Then he grabbed it in his mouth and started dragging it away. Suddenly, in some way, one of the legs of the tripod flew up and hit him. He jumped almost twenty feet. In a few minutes he came back to it, suspiciously at first; but when he saw that it did not move, he pounced on it.

What could we do? Not one of us would have budged out of the truck to retrieve any three-hundred-dollar camera. In a few minutes, a lioness left the zebra and came over to the other camera, which was still standing. She rubbed her head against it and chewed the wires that joined the cameras to the flares. We whistled and hissed to frighten her from it, but it did no good.

Finally, Dave yelled, "Scat, you silly lion, scat!"

Then Doug shouted, "Get away! We told you twice!"

The sound of our voices finally frightened the lioness from the camera and scared the others from the kill for a while. They soon returned, however, and went on with their meal.

We watched the lions for about an hour before we lay down again. Just as we decided to go to sleep, we heard a slight noise up in front of the truck. I grabbed my flashlight and crawled up to the partition that separated the front seat from the body. Shining my light through the bars, I saw the head of a lioness not three feet away! She had one foot on the fender and one on the floorboard; and she had stuck her head up on the seat. When she saw the light, she only blinked her eyes in a perplexed way and crawled back down in slow dignity.

We said not a word. It was the first time we had ever seen a lion try to drive our doorless truck, and the sight gave us quite a shock. We came back to our blankets wide awake and waited several minutes before we felt like turning in again. We lay there and strained our eyes and ears in the blackness. None of us cared to come any closer to lions in the wild than we had at that time. Though we all lay perfectly still, none of us slept for a long time.

In the morning when Mr. Johnston came over and woke us,

we told him about the night. He laughed for half an hour. If he lamented over the camera, we did not hear him. It did not seem to worry him. He said that our experience was worth it if the picture of the first lion turned out.

He and Mrs. Johnston had heard the lions roaring and growling over the kill. But they had never imagined we had seen seven lions.

When we returned to camp, Dave, Doug, and I could hardly stay awake. So after breakfast we lay down for a while.

About the middle of the morning when we woke up, Mr. Johnston took us over to where he developed his films. He wanted us to see the negative of the picture Dave had accidentally taken. We all felt sure that the lion was not in the right position, but when we saw the negative we were satisfied. Dave had caught the lion broadside, standing over the kill. Our adventure had brought some reward besides its thrills.

—Dick Douglas

"The sluggard will not plow by reason of the cold; therefore shall he beg in harvest, and have nothing."　　　Proverbs 20:4

Never Turned a Mill

Jake had really been around. He knew many things from the different places he had worked. But he had failed to learn one very important lesson. Can you discover what that was?

Many years ago a little stream ran through the forest. For hundreds of years it did nothing but splash and dash, gurgle and gush, as it bubbled along in the same channel it had followed from its beginning.

One day after settlers came to the land, a miller stopped to look at the stream as it splashed and dashed and gurgled and gushed along in its channel. The miller, who understood the language of streams, seemed to hear it babble, "I could work for you. I could work for you."

"Indeed, you could, little stream," he said, and an idea began to form in his mind. *All that splashing and dashing and gurgling and gushing could turn my water wheel. That water wheel could turn the stones to grind my grain.*

"What do you say, little stream? Are you **game** to go work in my mill?"

The little stream just kept splashing and dashing and gurgling and gushing, and the miller set to work to put his ideas in motion. He came with pick and shovel and wheelbarrow to put the little stream to work in his mill.

He dug a new channel for the stream. As he worked, he often stopped to pull out his bandana and mop the sweat from his brow. His pick sang its own melody as it struck rock after rock. Shovelful after shovelful of dirt filled up the wheelbarrow. Wheelbarrow after wheelbarrow built the dam that the miller used to **divert** the stream into the new channel he had created. Now the stream no longer flowed in its usual bed idly this way and that through the forest. The miller had directed it into the millrace. It had to flow through a narrow channel swift and strong over the waterwheel.

Now the people had a place to grind their grain into flour. In big sacks and small sacks, they brought their **grist** and waited till the miller ground it for them. Round and round moved the water wheel, turning the great millstones. Steadily, day after day, the little stream provided the power to grind sack upon sack of corn and wheat. Day in, day out, the stream flowed splashing and dashing, gurgling and gushing over the waterwheel to turn grist into flour for families far and near.

The neighborhood boys enjoyed taking their grist to the mill. The water splashing and dashing, gurgling and gushing over the waterwheel fascinated them. They loved to smell the freshly ground flour. The sound of the grinding tickled their ears. The noisy commotion of the mill attracted many of the boys on their way to and from school. Of course, the old miller added his own **zest** to the activity at the mill.

One morning a stranger came to the mill with George Kent when he brought his grist. Several boys stood in a group talking; and Jesse Smith sat on a bag of cornmeal reading.

"Hello everyone, meet Jake," called George, nodding toward the older boy with him. "He's our neighbor's new hired man."

Jesse looked up from his book to welcome the stranger. Seeing him, Jake exclaimed, "Studying, are you? My father wanted me to get a good education, but I never cared much for books. Dry old reading! Instead I went west. My uncle owns a ranch, and I persuaded him to hire me as an extra hand. I wanted to do something exciting like being a cowboy. Any sissy can sit around with his nose in a book."

"Water that runs at its own will is never known to turn a mill," said the old miller, who was tying up bags of flour and listening at the same time.

The boys looked around at him, but he didn't seem to be paying attention. They turned back to Jake, full of questions about his adventures out West.

"Were you really a cowboy?"

"Tell us about lassoing calves!"

"Did you ever brand cattle?"

"Hold on, hold on! I can't answer you all at once," replied Jake, obviously enjoying the attention. "I went along on the cattle drives and helped drive thousands and thousands of cattle being herded to the stock market."

"Oh, that sounds exciting," said Ralph wistfully. "I guess you enjoyed that life a lot!"

Jake shrugged. "Really, it was terribly dusty and boring. After the second cattle drive, I decided I had had enough of it. It was too much work to suit my tastes, so I quit."

"Water that runs at its own will is never known to turn a mill," said the old miller.

The boys turned again to look at him, but he went on tying up bags without stopping.

Then Jesse asked, "So now you've decided to try farming instead of ranching, is that it?"

"Well," Jake answered, "after I quit the ranch, Father put me in a machine shop. But it didn't take long to find out that I'm not very mechanically minded. Besides, about the only thing I did there was run errands for the boss. That got old pretty fast."

"Sounds like you prefer to boss yourself," commented George.

"Yep, that's a fact," answered Jake. "That's why I ran away."

"And turned up here," added Jesse, "to try your hand at farming. Well, my father says you have to stick at farming and work hard to make it a success,"

"Oh, I'm willing to try it at least a while," answered Jake. "I can always go somewhere else if it doesn't suit me."

"Water that runs at its own will is never known to turn a mill," said the old miller again.

This time Jake eyed the miller sharply. He looked as though he were trying to decide whether to laugh or to get angry. Watching, the other boys tried to hide their grins.

Albert spoke quickly. "My father says it doesn't matter whether it's fishing or farming—you have to stick with it to succeed. He says some parts of any job are fun and some are not so fun. Still, it takes all the parts—fun or not—to make a go of it. If you do the fun part and leave the rest, you'll never do anything worthwhile."

"That's the song of the stream," said the miller coming over to join the boys. *"Water that runs at its own will is never known to turn a mill.* The discipline of hard work and sticking at it prepares you to do well in any job."

"You sound like my dad," said Zeke. "He says it's good

experience for me to wash dishes, even though I hate it. I can't see any value in *that* when I want to take up carpentry. But Dad says the discipline of sticking to it, even when I don't care for it, will serve me well when I'm using a hammer and saw."

"And he's right," agreed the miller. "That will help you stick to your purpose just like the millrace keeps the water flowing straight over the wheel. Nobody ever amounts to anything in this life or the next by going this way and that way doing only as he pleases.

"Water that runs at its own will is never known to turn a mill," he said again.

The miller went back to his bags of flour; the boys hurried off to school. Jake wandered down by the stream and sat on the mossy bank. There the water splashed and dashed and gurgled and gushed. He thought he heard it singing, *"Water that runs at its own will is never known to turn a mill."*

Perhaps this is the song the millstream sang.

The Brook

I come from haunts of coot and hern,
    I make a sudden sally,
And sparkle out among the fern,
    To bicker down a valley.

By thirty hills I hurry down,   5
    Or slip between the ridges,
By twenty thorps, a little town,
    And half a hundred bridges.

Till last by Philip's farm I flow
    To join the brimming river,   10
For men may come and men may go,
    But I go on forever.

I chatter over stony ways,
    In little sharps and trebles,
I bubble into eddying bays,   15
    I babble on the pebbles.

With many a curve my banks I fret
    By many a field and fallow,
And many a lofty foreland set
    With willow-weed and mallow.   20

I chatter, chatter, as I flow
   To join the brimming river,
For men may come and men may go,
   But I go on forever.

I wind about and in and out,   25
   With here a blossom sailing,
And here and there a lusty trout,
   And here and there a grayling,

And here and there a foamy flake
   Upon me, as I travel   30
With many a silvery water-break
   Above the golden gravel,

And draw them all along, and flow
   To join the brimming river,
For men may come and men may go,   35
   But I go on forever.

I steal by lawns and grassy plots,
   I slide by hazel covers;
I move the sweet forget-me-nots
   That grow for flower-lovers.   40

I slip, I slide, I gloom, I glance,
   Among my skimming swallows;
I make the netted sunbeam dance
   Against my sandy shallows.

I murmur under moon and stars   45
   In brambly wildernesses;
I linger by my shingly bars,
   I loiter round my cresses;

And out again I curve and flow
   To join the brimming river,   50
For men may come and men may go,
   But I go on forever.

             –Alfred, Lord Tennyson

*"They that go down to the sea in ships, that do business
in great waters; these see the works of the LORD,
and his wonders in the deep."*   Psalm 107:23, 24

Underwater Fisherman

*You might go swimming to relax and enjoy the water.
To the boy in this story, swimming was part of his hard and
dangerous daily occupation.*

Harry Tolliver lounged day-dreaming as the little boats of
the sponge-fishing fleet headed out from Great Abaco[1] Island
in the Bahamas.[2] Today he turned twelve, and Mother would
have a special supper ready when he and his father came sailing back at sunset. She would have conch[3] chowder and sea
turtle steaks and cornbread covered with rich, sweet molasses.
And perhaps a bowl of candies.

Harry thought especially of the sea turtle steaks. Nothing
could be quite so good to eat anywhere on earth. Last night he
and his father had gone far along the shore to the **site** where
sea turtles laid eggs. They had lain among the beach-plum
bushes above the high tide mark. In silence, they watched the
moon rise like a great silver plate out of the ocean. Patiently

---
[1]Abaco – a′ bə kō
[2]Bahamas – bə hä′ məz
[3]conch – känk

183

they had waited and waited. At last, below them, where the little waves rolled up on the beach, a dark shape **emerged.** A sea turtle crawled slowly from the ocean.

Of all land turtles you have ever seen, you could hardly imagine one so large as this. Its great shell would have covered your teacher's desk. It weighed at least 200 pounds. Yet Harry and his father had seen many turtles of even greater size.

Soon more turtles emerged out of the sea up and down the shore. All of them labored **ponderously** across the sand to higher ground. Harry and his father watched as the turtles used their great webbed feet to scoop holes in the sand. They waited quietly while the turtles laid their eggs in the holes they had dug. Harry knew the hot sun of the summer days ahead would keep the sand warm around the eggs until they

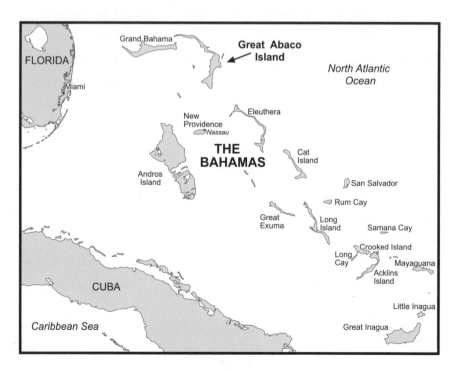

hatched. Then the baby turtles would emerge from the sand and scramble across the beach down toward the sea. Even though a sea turtle sometimes laid as many as 200 eggs at a time, many of the babies didn't live very long. As soon as the eggs began hatching, flocks of sea birds and land mammals would arrive, gobbling up the **miniature** turtles before they could reach the water. Even there fish might swallow them before they could grow to any size.

When Harry and his father saw the first turtle sweeping the sand back over her eggs, they rose quietly and ran swiftly toward her. Each carried a stout pole, and before the turtle could complete her ponderous journey back into the water, they had slipped the poles under her. Together they gave a mighty heave, and there lay the turtle kicking helplessly on her back. Now they could have fresh turtle steak at Harry's birthday supper.

A shout from his father awakened the slim boy from his pleasant daydreams. The boats had arrived at the site of the day's sponge fishing. Here they had come year after year, for they always **severed** the sponges carefully and knew that more had grown to take their places.

Down came the sail and over went the anchor. Quickly Harry picked up a wooden pail from the bottom of their boat and held it over the side with the bottom just beneath the surface of the water. Then leaning far over, he put his head almost completely into the pail.

Through the glass bottom of the pail, Harry could see all the way to the floor of the ocean, thirty feet below. There dozens of beautiful fish swam lazily about among great sweeping leaves of underwater plants. He could see the many colors of the limestone and coral that rose to within a few feet of the surface. And he could see sponges in all shapes and sizes.

Some of the strange animals looked like miniature castles with turrets and towers. Some looked like fans, and others resembled gloves. None of those interested Harry because he knew they had little value on the sponge market. He looked for the large well-rounded sponges that would bring high prices at the sale.

Harry put the pail back into the boat and slipped off his outer clothes. Around his waist he fastened a belt with a leather scabbard, sheathing his gleaming knife. Then taking a deep breath, over the side he went.

His clean dive left scarcely a ripple on the surface. Straight and powerful, it took him directly to the site of the sponges he had chosen while looking through the glass-bottomed pail. His keen knife flashed out. While his left hand held the sponge, his right hand swept the knife across the rock and severed the sponge from it.

A sticky, jelly-like substance filled the sponge, making it heavy. Harry clutched it tightly for fear it would slip from his hand and sink far beyond his reach. Then, with a quick glance to mark the next sponge, he gave a swift kick and shot up to the surface. There he tossed the sponge into the boat and filled his lungs with air.

His father gave a shout and held the sponge high for the other fishers to see. It was a large perfect sponge, a good beginning for the day.

All morning Harry worked. Occasionally he rested in the boat for a few minutes and drew great deep breaths of the clean tropic air. Most of the time, though, he swam beneath the surface searching out sponges.

At noon, after they had eaten their lunch, Harry lay back on the deck while his father told stories of their ancestors.

Centuries before, those people had set out to find a new home in the western world that Columbus had discovered. On the way, pirates had captured some of them and set them adrift in little boats on the open sea. Some they put ashore on lonely islands. Still others had been shipwrecked in storms as they sailed with Sir Walter Raleigh and his brave fleet.

Father told how those ancestors struggled to live without any of the comforts and conveniences of life. He told how they survived because they had learned to eat the strange new plants and fruit on the islands. He told how they had learned to build shelters that withstood the tropical storms, and had prospered until the rest of the world had found them again.

When Harry's father started the story of how their people came to be called "Conchs," he knew that it would soon be time to go back to work. That story always marked the end of lunch break.

Long ago the island people had discovered that the big spiral shells found in the sea housed a delicious creature. These creatures were called conchs, and because Harry's ancestors enjoyed eating them, strangers who travelled that way began to call the people Conchs. These travellers often bought the beautiful pink-and-white conch shells and took them home to far-away lands.

There they put them on their mantels, bookshelves, and tables—taking them down so the children could hold them to their ears and hear the sound of the sea.

At last Harry buckled on his knife belt and plunged again into the sea. As the day wore on, the mound of sponges grew in the little boat. As the boy severed the sponges growing on the coral reef, Harry's father began thinking of the good price they would bring after being cleaned and dried for the buyer.

While he worked, Harry thought about what the buyer had told him the last time he had come to the Bahamas. He had said that someone had found a way to shape the sponges to look like fish, and that now boys and girls in distant lands all wanted the fish sponges for their bathtubs.

Suddenly Harry felt a strange presence near him. A queer prickling warning crept up his spine. He glanced around, but saw nothing. Then a shadow swept over him—a squarish shadow with a thin tapering tail. A stingray! That creature which lives in tropic seas and which people dread! One lash of its barbed tail can cut deeply into your flesh. Worse yet, where that thin razor-sharp tail strikes, it leaves a poison almost as dangerous as a rattlesnake bite.

The ray had seen him; it hovered above the boy. Harry had no time to think, only to act. With a swift thrust against the wall of the reef, he shot up in front of the dreaded fish, away from that lashing tail. Swiftly his knife flashed, again and again. The water around turned a dull brown, and the ray disappeared.

His lungs bursting for want of air, Harry struggled to the surface.

At his gasping shout, his father hauled him quickly into the boat. When he could breathe easily again, he joined his father in looking through the glass-bottomed pail. Far below they could see a barracuda[4] tearing at the body of the giant ray.

An hour later the sponge-fishing boats set out for the home island. Many children waited at the wharf to see the day's crop of sponges. Harry and his father laid all their sponges out to dry before they started for home.

Conch chowder, sea turtle steaks, molasses-covered cornbread—no twelve-year-old ever enjoyed a birthday supper more than Harry did that night. As he drifted off to sleep, he felt sure that no one anywhere could have had such a happy day, because no one anywhere in all the world lived in such a wonderful part of God's earth as Great Abaco Island in the Bahamas.

—Don Henshaw

---

[4]barracuda – ber′ ə kü′ də

The Shell

A secret whorl
  of pink and cream.
The sound of the sea—
  a child's dream.

—Elizabeth Loeks Bouman

*"If a bird's nest chance to be before thee in the way in any tree,
or on the ground, whether they be young ones, or eggs, and the
dam sitting upon the young, or upon the eggs, thou shalt not
take the dam with the young."* Deuteronomy 22:6

The Water Ouzel Outwits an Enemy

*Since God sees every sparrow that falls, He surely had
His eye on this joyous water ouzel and the dark form slinking through the underbrush.*

The Water Ouzel[1] was fairly bursting with joy. He lived at
the beaver dam in a rocky canyon where a fork of the stream
came hurrying down the mountain valley. **Teetering** on a
boulder in the middle of the stream, he sang a merry song. Up
and down, up and down he dipped, as if tuned to the rising
and falling of ripples on water. His slate-gray feathers were
much more **somber** than his mood, but his tail was perky, like
a wren's.

This was a happy day! The Dipper sang of the fresh June
air of a mountain morning, of water tumbling over rocks, of
sunlight slanting through trees, making shadow-bridges across
the canyon. But most of all he sang of the little ones beginning
to hatch from the four white eggs in the mossy, ball-like nest

---

[1]ouzel – ü′ zəl

191

behind the waterfall. Already two baby ouzels had pecked their way out of their shells. Soon there would be two others. Oh, happy day!

Now it seemed a long time since the Ouzel's mate had laid those eggs, one each day for four days. And it seemed that she had been sitting on them, day and night, for a long time. But at last the babies were hatching! It was something to sing about.

A sudden shadow gliding down the stream sent the Ouzel into a dive, shattering his song. Was that a hawk's shadow? Or an eagle's? Not that it mattered, since both were enemies, though neither had ever gotten very close to the Dipper or his mate. A swoop of wings swept close to the water, but the chubby gray bird was safe by a wide margin as he half-ran, half-flew along the stream bed under a foot of water. He was perfectly at home under water. He had a third eyelid to protect his eyes, and his feathers were so close-fitting and well oiled that no moisture could get through them.

He pushed through a rush of current and popped **abrubtly** into the air. In a moment he was singing again, as he bobbed up and down on a rock. His quick eyes searched the canyon. Downstream on a broken stub a hawk perched. So that was the shadow he had seen! The Ouzel watched, unafraid. Watched and sang.

The hawk was watching, too, but its eyes were not on the perky bird whose song sounded above the noise of quick June water. Ripples of time moved by, ripples of water, before the Ouzel saw the hawk swoop down and pounce on something in the grass. It flew off with a mouse in its claws.

The Dipper was alone again with his song and the stream he loved. Yet not alone, either, for his mate was there in the felted nest behind the waterfall with their two young ones. Perhaps there were three by now!

In the midst of his song the Ouzel dived into the stream. He ran under water along the stony bottom, pushing himself with his wings where the current was swift. He found a slimy branch wedged between two rocks and gathered a beakful of water insects. Then he made a quick upward flip, fluttered his wings, and landed on a rock wet with spray. Yet he did not slip. He was as sure-footed as he was quick.

There on the rock the Dipper shook off beads of water from his feathers and teetered again before flying to his nest. He would bring the insects to his mate. Soon—soon they would both be busy finding water bugs and mosquito larvae for their four babies!

One more bob and he was off, flying upstream, right into the curtain of a little waterfall. He loved water, the cold, rushing, mountain water. He liked the feel of it against his waterproof feathers even more than he liked the feel of air.

He landed on the ledge in back of the waterfall, at the entrance to the bulky nest. How like a cushion of living moss it looked, with a film of spray keeping the outside fresh and green. Yet how warm and dry it was inside the padded walls. He poked his head into the little round door at the side and gave his mate the insects. She moved her feathers. Two baby heads, with huge open bills, appeared. Two white eggs were still unhatched. But soon—

For a moment the Ouzel bobbed up and down on the damp ledge outside his nest. He was proud of his mossy house they had built in April. They had woven it thickly of moss, leaves, pine needles, and fine grass, and they had cemented it in place with mud. It was beautifully **concealed!** The only way an enemy could reach it was by leaping an arm of the stream and slinking behind the waterfall. But how would an enemy know it was there in the first place?

The old nest farther upstream, the one he and his mate had used for two summers, was not safe any longer. A big spruce had crashed across the stream, making a bridge almost to the door.

The Ouzel flew through the waterfall curtain again, back into the bigness of the mountain world. He must bring his mate another mouthful, so she in turn could feed the babies. But first he must pour out more of his joy to the tumbling stream. He bobbed up and down and burst into song—loud and clear above the noise of the water.

But hold on—what was that? His sharp, white-rimmed eyes caught a shadowy movement on the shore, gliding to a slanting tree. He fixed his gaze on the spot as he sang. Now the shadow was moving along the tree, now it was gone, lost in the branches. What could it be? The Dipper kept watching and singing. Gradually out of the branches a face took shape—a round furry face with pointed ears and two glinting eyes. A bobcat!

The Ouzel dipped up and down. How long had the Bobcat been watching? Had she seen him flying through the waterfall with his mouth full of insects? Did she suspect his nest was there, with the young ones or the eggs the bobcat liked so well? He teetered on his rock.

For himself, the Ouzel was not afraid. Nor was he afraid for his mate. They could escape a wildcat any day. Few enemies could catch them as they darted through the quick water or dipped in and out among slippery rocks. But the new chicks and the eggs about to hatch—what would happen to them if the Bobcat discovered the nest? She could not possibly see it behind its veil of spray. Yet the Ouzel would have to keep bringing food. Those sly eyes would follow him. The enemy might well find a way to reach the nest behind the ledge.

The Dipper kept singing as if nothing could possibly be wrong with the bright June morning. Suddenly he dived into the stream again, in search of worms that lived under the loose gravel in the shallows. After a few moments he emerged on a rock upstream with his bill full. He was close to the waterfall now. But this time, instead of flying through the curtain of spray, he flew over it. Briefly he paused near the top of the falls on a partly sunken log. Was the Bobcat watching? Were those enemy eyes following him as he went upstream? Would she follow?

Now, keeping close to the water, so close that his wings almost touched it as he flew, he headed directly for the deserted nest. It was a bulging mossy cushion in the rocks. Thanks to a rainy spring, the outside was still green and mossy, and the oval fitted so well into the background it looked as if it grew there. By crossing on the fallen spruce, the Bobcat could reach the old nest without even wetting her feet.

The Ouzel poked his head into the entrance hole. He had

not been back for many months, not since the second brood of babies had flown from the nest last summer. He was surprised to see how different it looked. The thick walls were still firm and intact, but the inside was dirty with shucks and shells and husks of seeds. Mice must have taken over the nest for their winter home, though there was no evidence that they lived there now.

He gulped down his billful of food, and then lingered jauntily in front of the nest, bobbing up and down. He must entice the Bobcat away from the waterfall. His sharp eyes darted to the tree below the falls where he had seen her. Was she still there? It was hard to separate mottled fur from mottled shadows at this distance. But she seemed to be gone.

He dived into the stream again, into a deep place, and searched among the rocks. His strong feet with their sharp claws gave him sure balance against the current. His wings helped to propel him along. But this time, in his anxiety, he did not find anything to eat. He was in a hurry to get back to the old nest, to see if the Bobcat had followed him.

Shooting up out of the water, he flew to the ledge and teetered in front of the deserted nest. Then he broke into song, his bright eyes on the bank across the stream. Nothing happened, nothing moved except the small flicker of sun and shadow. He flew down to a dark red boulder in midstream and continued his song. Wait! A shadow was slinking through the brush on the bank. Now it paused.

The Ouzel hurried back to the ledge, and again poked his head into the old nest. Again he bobbed and sang in front of it as he watched the farther shore. The shadow was moving once more. Now with a leap it cleared the open space to the fallen tree. The Dipper jerked his perky tail and flew back to the wet boulder. He watched the enemy slide expertly through the stubs and branches of the "bridge," saw her leap lightly to the ledge.

Bending over the old nest, the Bobcat sniffed at it, then slapped it with her paw. The roof caved in, the mossy walls crumbled. Singing as he watched, the Dipper saw the Bobcat tear the nest apart and scatter the mouse litter. Her short stubby tail twitched angrily. She turned to glare and hiss at the little bird bobbing gaily on his rock. Then she jumped back to the fallen tree, leaped ashore, and disappeared in the woods.

The Ouzel interrupted his song to dive into the stream for a beakful of water bugs. They were not hard to find this time, for his anxiety was gone. He carried them to the nest behind the waterfall, and popped out, again full of singing. Dipping on his favorite rock, he sang of June and hatching eggs and baby birds with huge mouths. He sang of sunlight fingering the trees and of the nest hidden from enemy eyes. He even sang of the Bobcat who had failed to discover his secret. Oh, what a beautiful morning!

–Aileen Fisher

The Sandhill Crane

Whenever the days are cool and clear
The sandhill crane goes walking
Across the field by the flashing weir[1]
  Slowly, solemnly stalking.
The little frogs in the tules[2] hear   5
And jump for their lives when he
       comes near,
And minnows scuttle away in fear,
  When the sandhill crane goes
      walking.

---

[1]weir (wir) – dam in a stream or river
[2]tules (tū′ lēz) – plants that grow along
   the edges of and in water

The field folk know if he comes that way,
Slowly, solemnly stalking,   10
There is danger and death in the least delay
   When the sandhill crane goes walking.
The chipmunks stop in the midst of their play,
The gophers hide in their holes away
And "Hush, oh, hush!" the field mice say,   15
   When the sandhill crane goes walking.

                  –Mary Austin

"My little children, let us not love in word, neither in tongue; but in deed and in truth."

1 John 3:18

Just the Same Inside

What happens when a girl's love and determination are bigger than her ability to fulfill her dreams?

It was a beautiful shawl—Chi-weé[1] could see that from clear across the trader's store—dark blue on one side and glowing red on the other, with a fringe of the same two colors, and it looked warm and soft and *much* to be desired!

Chi-weé saw the entranced look in her mother's eyes as she passed her hand over its surface, and in her heart a fierce little voice said, with firm **resolution,** "My mother *shall have* that shawl—"

It was trading day for Chi-weé and her mother. In the early morning they had come in the sheepherder's wagon with the pottery jars that Chi-weé's mother had made. They would exchange them at the store for food and clothing.

Chi-weé dearly loved the long ride from the high **mesa** town to the canyon store in the bumpety old wagon. She enjoyed the ride over the wide desert of many changing colors and up and down sandy washes. She saw so many living things on the way:

---

[1]Chi-weé – chē wā´

prairie dogs and lizards and horned toads; sheep and, sometimes, away in the distance, an antelope or a gray coyote. They
had taken this ride together once a month in the same wagon
ever since Chi-weé had been old enough to sit by herself. The
wagon looked the same now as it had looked then.

Chi-weé came close to the shawl and felt it with her
fingers—it was as soft as it looked, and very warm.

"You will buy it, Mother?"

Her mother shook her head a little sadly.

"No, my little one," she said. "We must exchange the pottery
today for food and not for the things we do not need."

"But you *need* a shawl—*this* shawl," protested Chi-weé.
"You *know*, my mother, that you need it!"

"We will not speak of it more," said her mother, turning
away. "We have money for food only, my daughter." And she
spoke to the trader of the flour and grain and sugar that she
needed.

Chi-weé stood looking at the shawl, and above all the
thoughts churning in her mind, she repeated her resolution—"My mother *shall have* this soft, beautiful shawl."

She waited until her mother had carried some of the food
out to the wagon and then she went to the trader. He was a
congenial white man who had always spoken kindly to Chi-
weé, so she had no fear of him.

"How much does that shawl cost?" she asked him, "the soft
blue one with the red underside?"

"Six dollars," answered the trader, with a kindly smile for
Chi-weé. "It is all wool and very warm."

A thoughtful look came into Chi-weé's eyes. Her hand went

201

to her pocket where she carried her special treasure. "Look," she said softly to the trader. "See this very beautiful string of shells. Look, they are the color of the sky when the sun comes up pink. I—I think it is very beautiful."

The trader stooped and looked at it.

"Yes," he nodded with a congenial smile. "I would give you two dollars for it, if you cared to sell it."

Her face fell and she touched the pink shells tenderly.

"Two dollars? I—I—thought—you see—I want the shawl for my mother," she blurted out.

"I am sorry," said the trader gently, "but the shawl is worth more, little girl. No, I could not exchange it for your shells."

Chi-weé felt her heart grow very heavy, and all the way home in the bumpety wagon she had no eyes for the lizards and the little hares and the prairie dogs that scuttled out of her way, nor for the wonderful colors of the tumbleweeds and the cactus, or the far-away blue **buttes.** She must earn money for the wonderful shawl. She *must.* But how could she do it?

There were so few ways to earn money in the high mesa town. She could weave a very little—an old man in the pueblo had taught her that—but that took a long time and money, too, to buy the colored wools. She could not make pottery well enough to sell. She could pick peaches and apricots, but now was not the time for them, and anyway they gave her but a few pennies in exchange for her work. And she had nothing to sell—nothing but her beautiful string of shells, her one treasure—and the trader had told her it was worth only two dollars—and the shawl cost six! Oh, but it was a very difficult thing, this earning money—she could not understand how other people did it. But not for a moment did she give up the thought of getting the shawl for her mother—it was just *how* to get it that puzzled her.

When next they went to the trader's, Chi-weé looked eagerly for the shawl and she felt that her heart almost stopped beating when she did not see it where it had been before. Of course others would see its beauty and purchase it; others who had six dollars and even more.

"Did you sell it?" she asked the trader, in a voice that quivered with anxiety. "That—beautiful shawl—has it been sold?"

He looked at her for a moment with a perplexed frown on his face. "The shawl?" he asked, and then recollection dawned in his eyes as he laughed a little. "No, I didn't sell it—did you want to buy it?"

A sudden resolution came into Chi-weé's heart—it almost frightened her.

"Yes," she said quickly, and looked to see that her mother was beyond hearing, "I want to buy it—but I do not have the money—not *all* now. Here!" and with trembling hands she thrust the string of beautiful shells into his hand, "I will bring more next time. Could you keep it a little while for me?"

There was such an eagerness in the voice, such a look in the eyes, and such a tremble all through the small figure that the trader could not help noticing it. The surprised expression in his eyes softened, and he put his hand on Chi-weé's black head.

"How old are you, little girl?" he asked, unexpectedly.

"Seven, I think," answered Chi-weé, in a surprised voice.

"My mother tells me—yes, she tells me, seven."

"Ah," said the man, slowly, with a tender far-away look in his eyes. "Yes," he added, with sudden resolution his voice, "I will keep the shawl for you until you bring the rest of the money or something in exchange," and he turned to the others who had entered the store.

Chi-weé felt as if she walked on air as she went to the wagon. The shawl was hers—*hers*—almost! And *almost* was such a little word that she nearly forgot it altogether. Those warm, soft folds would rest upon her mother's shoulders, and that lovely red would gleam as she walked—and how happy Chi-weé would feel that *she* had bought and paid for it herself. But her heart dropped a little at the thought. How *was* she going to pay for it?

Chi-weé must have **devised** some sort of plan, for had her mother not been very occupied with her own work during the next month she would have noticed something strange about Chi-weé's actions. She would have wondered why her daughter made so many unexplained trips into the desert. She would have wondered what Chi-weé concealed each time she returned. Even when the next trading day came, Mother did not notice the bump under the girl's shawl as they rode to the canyon store. She was outside unloading her things when Chi-weé handed the trader a great jar of wild honey. Her heart beat fast with excitement and happiness. She did not tell of the labor she had had in getting it nor of the painful lumps on her arm that told of the angry stinging of bees, but her voice rang with deep satisfaction as she said:

"I have brought this to pay some more for the shawl—next time we come I will bring something else."

A look she could not understand came into the trader's eyes as he took the honey, but he turned quickly from her and spoke to a white stranger standing near. She could not catch the words, and when he turned back to her she could not understand his expression. But his next words shattered her happiness.

"I have other shawls," she suddenly heard him saying to her. "You will not mind that this gentleman has bought the blue one with the red underside?"

To Chi-weé it seemed as if the world turned black—her shawl—her mother's shawl—to go to this stranger! She could not speak—words would not come—and everything began to swim through the sudden tears in her eyes. In a blur, she saw the strange man walk to the door with the bundle under his arm. The trader turned his back to attend to those who waited at his counter. It could not be true—people could not be so cruel as that!

Chi-weé stumbled out of the store and climbed into the waiting wagon, numb with anger and grief. But she did not cry. She sat in somber silence all the way home and tried to think why white people did things that no Indian could ever do.

At their home door her mother called to her to help with the parcels in the wagon. "And take this great one," she said, "that the white stranger said you had bought from the trader. How could you buy anything, little daughter?"

Chi-weé opened her eyes wide and stood still. "I did not buy anything," she stammered, bewildered. What could it mean? Her mother placed a great bundle wrapped in white paper into her arms.

She did not wait to ponder, but right there before her door she tore open the parcel. *There lay the shawl—her shawl!* And tied to one corner was a little card with words printed on it in ink—she could read them with difficulty:

"Your love for your mother has bought this shawl, little girl of the mesa. And my love for another little girl like you gives you back your precious treasure. White hearts are just the same as Indian ones, inside!"

And there, beside the shawl, wrapped in a bit of paper, Chi-weé found her beautiful string of pink shells!

Now Chi-weé *did* cry—tears just for happiness. And she hugged the shawl, and her mother, who did not yet understand!

She did not know then or afterwards whether the congenial trader or the stranger had given her the shawl, because the trader would not say. But to Chi-weé it did not matter, for she had learned a great secret, that "White hearts are just the same as Indian ones, inside!"

– Grace Purdie Moon

206

as my eyes
search
the prairie
I feel the summer
in the spring   5

   – a Chippewa Indian song

Indian Boy

All day the Indian boy
Watches his sheep.
The young lambs run,
The young lambs leap.
The boy sits dreaming   5
All day long,
His sheep his friends,
The wind his song.

— Johnny Sloan

"I will not put forth mine hand against my lord;
for he is the LORD's anointed."   1 Samuel 24:10

I Will Not Do It

King Saul had tried several times to kill David. He even
pursued David with an army. David knew that he was to
become king after Saul died. Now David had a chance to
kill Saul. What would he do?

¹ And it came to pass, when Saul was returned from following the Philistines,¹ that it was told him, saying, Behold, David is in the wilderness of Engedi.² ² Then Saul took three thousand chosen men out of all Israel, and went to seek David and his men upon the rocks of the wild goats.

³ And he came to the sheepcotes by the way, where was a cave; and Saul went in to cover his feet: and David and his men remained in the sides of the cave. ⁴ And the men of David said unto him, Behold the day of which the LORD said unto thee, Behold, I will deliver thine enemy into thine hand, that thou mayest do to him as it shall seem good unto thee. Then David arose, and cut off the skirt of Saul's robe privily.

⁵ And it came to pass afterward, that David's heart smote

---

¹Philistines – fə lis' tēnz
²Engedi – en ged' ī

him, because he had cut off Saul's skirt. ⁶And he said unto his men, The LORD forbid that I should do this thing unto my master, the LORD's anointed, to stretch forth mine hand against him, seeing he is the anointed of the LORD. ⁷So David stayed his servants with these words, and suffered them not to rise against Saul.

But Saul rose up out of the cave, and went on his way. ⁸David also arose afterward, and went out of the cave, and cried after Saul, saying, My lord the king. And when Saul looked behind him, David stooped with his face to the earth, and bowed himself.

⁹And David said to Saul, Wherefore hearest thou men's words, saying, Behold, David seeketh thy hurt? ¹⁰Behold, this day thine eyes have seen how that the LORD had delivered thee to day into mine hand in the cave: and some bade me kill thee: but mine eye spared thee; and I said, I will not put forth mine hand against my lord; for he is the LORD's anointed.
¹¹Moreover, my father, see, yea, see the skirt of thy robe in my hand: for in that I cut off the skirt of thy robe, and killed thee not, know thou and see that there is neither evil nor transgression in mine hand, and I have not sinned against thee; yet thou huntest my soul to take it.

¹²The LORD judge between me and thee, and the LORD avenge me of thee: but mine hand shall not be upon thee. ¹³As saith the proverb of the ancients, Wickedness proceedeth from the wicked: but mine hand shall not be upon thee.

¹⁴After whom is the king of Israel come out? after whom dost thou pursue? after a dead dog, after a flea. ¹⁵The LORD therefore be judge, and judge between me and thee, and see,

and plead my cause, and deliver me out of thine hand.

¹⁶ And it came to pass, when David had made an end of speaking these words unto Saul, that Saul said, Is this thy voice, my son David? And Saul lifted up his voice, and wept. ¹⁷ And he said to David, Thou art more righteous than I: for thou hast rewarded me good, whereas I have rewarded thee evil. ¹⁸ And thou hast shewed this day how that thou hast dealt well with me: forasmuch as when the LORD had delivered me into thine hand, thou killedst me not. ¹⁹ For if a man find his enemy, will he let him go well away? wherefore the LORD reward thee good for that thou hast done unto me this day.

²⁰ And now, behold, I know well that thou shalt surely be king, and that the kingdom of Israel shall be established in thine hand. ²¹ Swear now therefore unto me by the LORD, that thou wilt not cut off my seed after me, and that thou wilt not destroy my name out of my father's house.

²² And David sware unto Saul. And Saul went home; but David and his men gat them up unto the hold.

−1 Samuel 24

PEOPLE LIKE YOU AND ME

Some People I Know

Some people I know like to chatter,
while others speak hardly a word;
some think there is nothing the matter
with being completely absurd;
some are impossibly serious,
while others are absolute fun;
some are reserved and mysterious,
while others shine bright as the sun.

Some people I know appear sour,
but many seem pleasant and sweet;
some have the grace of a flower,
while others trip over their feet;
some are as still as a steeple,
while some need to fidget and fuss;
yet every last one of these people
is somehow exactly like us.

—Jack Prelutsky

*"Whoso diggeth a pit shall fall therein: and he that rolleth a
stone, it will return upon him."*   Proverbs 26:27

Boomerang

*A tattletale ought to be punished. Especially when he
tries to get his friends into trouble. It would be easy: a surprise attack, two against one. Ray and Abner were sure
their plan couldn't fail. They'd teach someone a never-to-
be-forgotten lesson.*

The soft, wet snow drifted down like lazy feathers. Thomas
stepped out into it, book in one hand, lunch pail in the other.
He glanced about the school playground, but seeing no one,
turned toward home. He walked rapidly for a few steps, then
broke into an easy run. The fluffy snow melted on his face and
trickled down his cheeks.

Straining to see through the blurry whiteness all around
him, Thomas made out the dim figures of his two friends,
Abner and Ray. He soon overtook them.

"Oh, hello, Thomas," greeted Ray. "Where were you?"

"Aw, I forgot my speller," said Thomas, breathing heavily. "I
had to run back after it. Can't see how I forgot it—with that
exam tomorrow."

At the mention of the spelling exam, Abner and Ray glanced
at each other and grinned. Abner shifted his schoolbag into

the same hand that held his lunch pail. With his free hand he brushed the clinging snow from his shoulders. He winked knowingly at Ray.

"So you're worried about spelling tomorrow, Thomas?"

"Not exactly worried. But I know I'll have to do some studying tonight."

"Fifty words aren't very many," Abner said. "That's Miss Kuhns' usual number for exams. It won't take you long to study fifty words." He winked at Ray again.

Thomas shook the snow from the top of his lunch pail. "Of course, fifty words wouldn't be bad, if I knew which fifty. But that's how it is with a spelling exam—you've got to study all the words to get the right fifty."

Abner's eyes danced as he glanced around to see if anyone were near. "Would you like to know *which* fifty to study?" he asked.

"Huh? What do you mean? What good would it do if I did want to know?"

"Oh," said Abner in an offhanded manner, as though he were merely discussing the weather, "you might ask me and I would tell you."

"All right," Thomas said, "tell me, Prophet Abner. Which fifty words will our teacher, Miss Kuhns, pronounce for the sixth grade spelling exam tomorrow?"

"I declare," said Abner in an official tone, "that Miss Kuhns will open the speller at *Week Nine,* and that she will begin to pronounce the words at the top of the page; moreover, she will follow the list to the next pages until she has fifty.

"Behold, I speak the truth," he said, making an impressive

flourish with his right hand and bowing grandly. "I speak the truth and it will surely come to pass."

Thomas and Ray laughed. "I wish I could believe him," Thomas said to Ray, "and although I hate to hurt his feelings, I greatly fear he is a false prophet."

"No, I'm serious," Abner said. "I happen to know she will give us those exact words."

"Really?"

"Sure."

"Aw, I don't believe it," Thomas declared. "You couldn't know that."

"But he does," broke in Ray eagerly. "Abner saw Miss Kuhns' test schedule, and that was what she had marked."

"When did he see it?" asked Thomas, still uncertain.

"This very morning." Ray looked at Abner.

"It's true," Abner said. "Miss Kuhns had left her books and things on the bench in the hall. They were just lying there when I came, so I took the chance to peek a little. It was obvious which words she plans to give us."

"It's a wonder you didn't get caught snooping," Thomas said.

"Ho, I kept my eyes open." Abner scooped up a handful of snow and packed it into a hard ball. "I wasn't about to get caught. Too smart for that." He threw the snowball at a telephone pole, striking it in the very center. "All you gotta do is study those fifty words and you'll get a good grade."

The boys walked more slowly now, for they were almost at Thomas's home.

"I don't know," Thomas said **apprehensively.** "What if Miss

Kuhns finds out? Anyway, that sounds almost like cheating."

"What's cheating about it?" Abner asked airily. "It's not cheating. I'm sure of that—just as sure as I'm going to hit that dog up there with my snowball."

Abner drew back his arm and with sure aim the icy ball sailed into the unsuspecting ribs of Mr. Dexter's black dog crossing the road ahead of them. The startled animal went yapping for home.

Thomas laughed. "Well, that's pretty sure, all right. You're a good shot, but I'm still not convinced that this other thing is straight. I wish you hadn't even told me which words we're having." The boys had paused at the end of Thomas's lane.

"If that's the way you feel about it, there's no harm done. You can just go ahead and study all the words if you want to. But I can tell you, it isn't cheating. You wouldn't be copying from anyone else at all. You'd have to know how to spell every one of those words yourself. That's what the teacher wants, isn't it?"

"I guess she does, but—"

"Then you needn't call it cheating. Anyway, she shouldn't have left her books lying out there in the hall."

"But she trusts us. She didn't expect anyone to snoop into her things. But it still seems—it can't be a fair—a fair exam, if we know which words to study. That's just like a regular lesson, not an exam. It can't be honest."

"I wouldn't know why not," Abner replied impatiently, though he looked a bit embarrassed at Thomas's words. "If we're smart enough to find out which words we're getting, we deserve a good grade. You can study all the words if you want,

217

but you won't catch me being so stupid." As the two of them walked away, Abner muttered to Ray, "Thomas sure likes to study better than I do!"

Thomas made up his mind to study *all* his spelling words, not just the fifty Abner had said they would have on the test. But he found it almost impossible. Again and again he caught himself studying at *Week Nine* and the pages right after it. He studied until late, but when he went to bed he knew he had not been completely honest—he had studied those fifty words more than the rest.

"I guess I'm just being too fussy. After all, it isn't really cheating." That's what he told himself, but in his heart he knew that even if it wasn't exactly cheating, there was still something wrong about it. He tossed on his bed, unable to sleep. Miss Kuhns trusted them. *What if she finds out!*

He rolled over. If it wasn't dishonest, why did he feel so apprehensive? Thomas couldn't find a comfortable position anywhere. He closed his eyes but couldn't sleep. All he saw was Miss Kuhns standing before them the day exams began. "Boys and girls, these tests are to help you as well as me." He remembered every word she had said. "Exams show where you need more study; and if you do your work dishonestly you're just being unfair to yourself. When you cheat, you're cheating yourself more than anyone else.

"But there's a more important reason for honesty." Thomas remembered that Miss Kuhns had looked very serious then. "And that is the effect it will have in your life both now and later. Right now you are forming habits that will make you into the kind of person you will be in a few years. If you think a little dishonesty doesn't matter now, how about when you are an adult? Do you plan to be a man or woman who is a little dishonest or who does a little cheating now and then? What kind of men and women do you want to be when you grow up?" The classroom had grown very quiet when Miss Kuhns said this.

"Of course, the most important reason is that God requires honesty. The Bible tells us to provide things honest in the sight of all men."

Thomas rolled over again and buried his head deep in his pillow, pondering his problem. He didn't want to **expose** Abner's snooping. He dreaded to think of the consequences for his friends if he tattled on them. Yet he knew that he'd never feel right if he took that test knowing what the words were.

Sometime I'd have to tell Miss Kuhns, he mused miserably. *Confessing later will be ten times harder than doing something now. But what?*

Suddenly he jerked up his head. He had thought of a way. "I'll do it," he declared resolutely. With a sigh, he turned over and dropped off to sleep.

More snow fell during the night, and when Thomas stepped from the house early the next morning, he could see no signs of Abner and Ray having passed. He was glad, because he wanted to talk to Miss Kuhns alone.

Thomas hurried between the tall hedges planted on each side of the walk leading to the schoolhouse door. Someone had already shoveled the snow from the walk, piling it high on either side and leaving only a narrow strip of concrete to mark the path.

Entering the building, Thomas found Miss Kuhns at her desk. Otherwise the room was deserted. "Good morning, Thomas," she greeted, with her usual congenial smile.

"Good morning."

Thomas left his lunch on the shelf at the back of the room, then took his speller to his desk. Hesitantly he walked over to Miss Kuhns and stood shyly in front of her desk.

She looked up. "Yes?"

"I—I have some—I mean—there's something I want to tell you." There! It was out.

He was still talking with the teacher a few minutes later when he heard the door open. He glanced back and saw Abner and Ray putting their lunches on the shelf. Thomas saw Abner nudge Ray before they turned and left. The way they looked at him made him uneasy.

He turned back to the teacher. "Miss Kuhns, I—I—wish you wouldn't try to find out who did it because that's not why I told you. It's because I knew I studied those words more than the others, and whatever grade I got would be kinda like I stole it."

"Thanks for telling me," Miss Kuhns said with a smile. "You did the right thing. I'll just choose other words. Perhaps I should insist that you tell me who snooped into my lesson plans, but I'll let it pass since you asked me to. I've learned that dishonest students expose themselves sooner or later."

Classes proceeded that day without incident. Miss Kuhns gave them the test but made no mention of having changed her schedule. From his desk near the back, Thomas could see that Abner and Ray were not taking the test as confidently as they had expected. And he could see that they were angry. He tried to speak with them at noon, but they carefully avoided him.

I'll explain on the way home tonight, Thomas thought. *And if they're still angry, they'll just have to be; I did the best I knew.*

Before she dismissed school that evening, Miss Kuhns said, "Thomas, I would like to send a note along with you for Mr. Dexter. Would you mind waiting after school until I write it? I want him to make some repairs on the playground." Mr. Dexter, the part-time janitor, lived next door to Thomas.

I wish Abner and Ray would wait for me, Thomas thought when the other pupils filed out and he stayed for Mr. Dexter's note. *I wish they would, but they likely won't. They probably won't forgive me for a long time.*

He did not know that Abner and Ray *were* waiting for him.

"Let's give that Thomas a snowballing he won't forget," Abner fumed to Ray as they left the school. "He's some friend—running to the teacher and tattling after we tried to help him. I'm sure I flunked that old test."

"Me too. She didn't give us a single one of the words we studied. And we didn't study a single one of the words she gave us. But why didn't she keep us in?" Ray sounded perplexed. "I can't believe she let us out this afternoon."

"Don't relax too soon. We'll catch it yet. We won't get by without a punishment of some sort—I know Miss Kuhns better than that! She's just waiting until tomorrow. After she grades the tests, she'll have proof that we didn't study all the words. Then we'll catch it for sure," surmised Abner in gloomy apprehension.

"Maybe she thinks if she waits a while we'll forget who told on us. Just like her to be looking out for Thomas. But at least we'll have settled the score with him. *He'll* know we didn't forget."

The more the boys discussed it, the more wronged they felt.

"Here," directed Abner, "let's hide behind this bush and wait for him. We can hear the door bang when he comes out. As soon as he steps clear of the hedge, let's bomb him with snowballs." Quickly the boys stockpiled a heap of hard-packed snowballs and positioned themselves out of sight.

At last they heard the schoolhouse door open and slam shut. "He's coming," hissed Abner. "Get ready. Just as he steps from behind the hedge, let him have it."

The two boys crouching in ambush could not see Thomas coming. But they could hear footsteps—closer and closer.

"Remember, the moment he steps past the end of the hedge—sh–sh—"

The boys waited breathlessly.

"Now!" Two carefully aimed snowballs whizzed through the air and caught their victim completely by surprise.

Abner's powerful throw caught Miss Kuhns in the shoulder and spun her half around. Ray's snowball crashed into her hand, knocking a book from her fingers.

Both boys froze in stunned consternation. Then words poured out in stuttering dismay. "Oh, Miss Kuhns, we're—we're sor—sorry. We're sorry. We didn't—didn't mean to do it—really, we—w-we didn't. We didn't know it was you."

The startled teacher stood speechless. For a long moment she stood there, scrutinizing the stammering boys and rubbing her hand where the snowball had struck. Then she stooped to retrieve her book.

"If you are so sorry," she said, finding her voice, "why did you do it?"

"We—we thought it was Thomas," blurted Ray. "We thought it was Thomas," he repeated, fearful that she would not believe him.

"Thomas!" exclaimed Miss Kuhns. "Why did you want to hurt Thomas?"

Humiliated, the two boys hung their heads. "I guess we got mad," Abner finally said. "We got mad because he squealed on us about the spelling exam."

Miss Kuhns stared at the boys in front of her. Her searching eyes seemed to look right through them.

"Boys," she began slowly. "Thomas did tell me someone found out what words I planned to give you, but he didn't mention any names. He asked me not to try to find out, so I planned to let it pass. You obviously forgot that those who cheat, cheat themselves." Miss Kuhns paused and the boys shifted uneasily, wishing they were somewhere else.

"The other students studied all the words. Now they probably know how to spell most of them. You boys studied only fifty. When I looked over your papers a while ago, it was obvious that you cheated yourselves out of knowing how to spell all those other words. Not only that, but when you see your scores, you'll realize you also cheated yourselves out of good grades.

"I should also have told you," Miss Kuhns paused again, "that those who aim to hurt others, often hurt themselves.

223

Since you have given yourselves away, you will have to face the consequences. Come back to the schoolhouse. We may as well settle this right now."

– Elmo Stoll

Dare to Be True

Dare to be true;
   Nothing can need a lie.
The fault that needs one most
   Grows two thereby.

—George Herbert

*"**W**herefore putting away lying, speak every man truth with his neighbor."*

Jelly Beans Forever

Bert felt positive that a boy who hadn't gone to school would not know anything that he didn't know. He was so sure that he chose his own penalty if he were proved wrong.

"I could eat jelly beans forever," Bert Baxter remarked to his twin sister, Becky, as he plunged his hand into the bag on the porch step between them.

"Don't **exaggerate**," admonished Becky. "I think exaggerations are idle words, and you know what the Bible says about *them.*"

Bert tossed a handful of jelly beans into his mouth and shifted them to both cheeks before answering. "Yes, I know; but that's not stretched much. Anyway, I could eat them all afternoon, and that's what I wish I could do instead of going with you and Daddy," he **retorted.**

"But he is so eager to have us meet that little fellow who thought he had to wear shoes to Daddy's meetings. You know the one who picked blackberries to sell to buy shoes, and then spilled them when his mule jumped away from a black snake."

"Yes, I know the whole story, but it's too hot to walk any-where, and we can't drive to his house. Anyhow, that Chad what's-his-name won't be anything special to see. I wouldn't miss a thing if I never saw him or his poky old mule." Bert reached into the jelly bean bag again. He sorted through his handful, dropping the purple ones back into the bag. "These purple ones," he exclaimed with a disgusted **grimace,** chang-ing the subject. "There are two things I'd like to know about the people who make them. First, do they really flavor them with varnish, and second, do they think anyone eats the things?"

"And there are two things I'd like to know about you," said Becky, as she took the bag and shook the purple ones aside before helping herself. "One is, why you are so grouchy about going along this afternoon, and the other is, whether you think I like those old purple ones any better than you do."

Bert laughed, then said, "Oh, I have no real reason for not wanting to go, only I wanted to read the new *Popular Mechanics* that came today. And I'm grouchy because it's so hot, and we'll have blisters by the time we climb up and down that mile-high mountain.

"Don't exaggerate," Becky said again. "Really, Bert, I think exaggerating is sort of like lying, and Christians don't even sort-of-lie, you know."

"Aw, come on, Becky, why be so particular? You don't really think exaggerating is all that serious, do you?"

"Yes, I really do, because it's not being altogether truthful."

"Then I'm sure you are the only one in the whole wide world who—" Bert caught himself and laughed a bit **sheepishly.**

"There you go again," Becky said severely. "See what a terrible habit you have."

"Maybe so," Bert agreed carelessly. "But only a girl would make a fuss about such a little thing. You'd never find a boy so particular."

"I'm not going to argue," Becky retorted, "but I do wish you'd go along with Daddy and me. Maybe it will be cooler in the mountains. Besides, you can read *Popular Mechanics* any time. More than likely Chad could teach you some things you'll never find in *Popular Mechanics.*"

"Like what?" challenged Bert.

"I don't know," admitted his sister, "but I believe he could."

"And I believe he couldn't. Daddy said he never even went to school."

"That doesn't matter. There are lots of things to know that aren't written in books. Likely he knows plenty you don't."

"All right, I'll go along and keep my eyes open, and we'll see how smart this Chad what's-his-name is. Furthermore, I'll eat ten purple jelly beans for everything he mentions that is news to me."

"Don't exaggerate," Becky said for the third time.

"I'm not exaggerating. I mean it," Bert insisted.

Becky smiled wisely. "I just may have occasion to remind you of that promise before the day is over," she said.

The afternoon found Bert and Becky trudging up the mountain. Their father showed them the little store where he had first met Chad. Then he pointed out the spot where Slow Girl, Chad's mule, had spilled the precious berries.

After a long, hot trek up a steep trail, they stood panting at the edge of a large clearing. "A real log cabin!" breathed Becky delightedly, as they came within sight of Chad's home.

Two bony, brown hounds bayed a welcome that brought a tiny old lady to the open doorway. "Howdy, howdy," she called. "I just had a feelin' someone would come today. And I sure am glad to see you again, Preacher. Come on up and set. Chad, bring two more chairs."

A wiry, overalled boy appeared from within the house, carrying two cane-bottomed chairs. From under his wavy yellow hair, great brown eyes looked at them guardedly. The twins instantly noticed an awkward white bandage that covered one ear.

"Howdy," he said, placing the chairs, then taking a seat on the porch steps.

After introducing the children, Daddy and Chad's grandmother were soon chatting away, while Becky and Bert and Chad sat silently pretending not to see each other.

Finally the old lady suggested, "Chad, why don't you take Bert and Becky to see Slow Girl? Maybe they'd like to ride her."

"C'mon," Chad said, leading the way across the bare yard. The twins followed silently. But, out of hearing of the adults, Bert found his voice.

"What happened to your ear?" he asked, indicating the bandage.

Chad laughed sheepishly. "Don't really need the bandage, but Granny makes me wear it." He lifted a strip of adhesive tape to expose a deep ragged tear in the tender part of his ear. "Caught it on a possum hanger. 'Tweren't more'n a scratch."

He pressed the tape into place again and went on.

Behind Chad's back Becky and Bert frowned at each other in bewilderment. Suddenly Becky's face broke into a wide smile. She raised both hands with the fingers spread wide. "Ten purple jelly beans," she mouthed at her brother.

Bert grimaced and turned his back on her.

After plunging down a steep slope through sumac and scrubby pines, Chad stopped. "There she is," he announced.

"Where?" Bert asked, craning his neck in all directions.

"Over there by the stake and rider," Chad pointed.

"Oh, I see her now. Who did you say is riding her?"

"No one," Chad looked a bit puzzled. "But we can if y'all want to."

"I sure would. Let's go over there," Bert suggested, starting out. He had an uncomfortable feeling that Becky was trying to catch his eye.

She was. When Chad left them to walk over and hook an arm around Slow Girl's neck, Becky said in a low voice, "Stake and rider is a fence—a rail fence, Brainy One. I know that much myself."

Bert frowned and walked away, while Becky sang, "Twenty purple jelly beans," under her breath to the tune of "Mary Had a Little Lamb."

Riding Slow Girl proved to be fun. They guided her by a cord Chad tied to her halter, and made her go by banging their heels into her ribs. But none of them could get her to go faster than a walk.

Then they sat on the brown carpet of needles under a pine tree and talked.

"Are there any wild animals around here?" asked Bert. "Bear or deer or anything like that?"

"No deer, but some bear, and once in a while we hear a painter."

"A painter? What's that?" inquired Becky.

"That's the same as a panther, isn't it?" Bert put in quickly.

"Yes, and some folks call them mountain lions."

Bert flashed his twin a triumphant look that said, "You didn't catch me on that one."

Then Becky began asking questions. "Chad, what do you do all the time up here? Isn't it lonesome with no one to play with?"

"No, I'm never lonesome. I like it up here. I work mostly, but sometimes I go fishing or hunting. Then we go to meetin'. Ever since your pa preached here, we go to meetin' whenever we can. Granny says we must learn what the Bible says so we know how to live right. She says we must be partikler about doing some things, and about not doing other things—stealin' and lyin' and such. That's what your pa said God wants us to do; and I know your pa's no lying man."

"No, he isn't," Bert agreed readily, in a thoughtful tone.

"Well, I don't want to be no lyin' man when I grow up, either, do you? Lyin's one thing I know is plumb wrong. Granny's whaled me often enough for lyin', so I'm plenty partikler about *that,* I can tell you!"

A dull red color crept into Bert's face, and he avoided Becky's eyes as he asked quickly, "What do you do when the weather's bad?"

"Oh, then I play my dulcimer."

"A dulcimer?" put in Becky. "Never heard of that; have you, Bert?"

"Well, isn't it some kind of loom you use to weave rugs?" Bert spoke uncertainly, and scowled into Becky's impish face when the mountain boy wasn't looking.

"No," answered Chad. "It's an instrument, sort of like a guitar or a banjo, but not as many strings."

"Oh, I see. Uh,—uh, what animals do you hunt?"

"'Coon and rabbit and squirrel and 'possum, mostly."

"Do you use a gun?"

"Yes, for all but the rabbits. I make deadfalls for them. It saves shells," replied Chad.

"Deadfalls?" Bert was genuinely interested. Becky started to hum the tune to "Mary Had a Little Lamb," again. Bert ignored her and turning to Chad, asked, "Could you show me how you make them and how they work? I never saw one."

"Sure. Let's go to the house. I'll need an ax."

An hour later Daddy could hardly get Bert started down the mountain toward the car. But finally good-byes were said, and they left. As they walked along the trail, Daddy asked, "What are you carrying those sticks for, Bert?"

"This is for a deadfall. Want to see how it works?" Bert knelt in the trail and, after selecting a heavy flat stone, demonstrated the deadfall.

Becky watched with interest, but under her breath she was singing, "Forty purple jelly beans."

Her brother ignored her while he showed how the stone was balanced and where to place the bait.

Late that evening the twins again sat on the porch steps. Bert was unusually quiet, but Becky didn't notice. She was shaking the jelly bean bag, picking out the despised varnish-flavored purple ones and placing them beside Bert.

"There are your beloved jelly beans," she said at last, giving the bag a final shake. "After all your big talking, did you learn anything new from Chad this afternoon or didn't you?"

"Yes, Becky," Bert's voice was unexpectedly humble. "I learned more than you might think. I learned that the Lord isn't pleased when I exaggerate. I don't want to be a lying man when I grow up, and from now on I'm not going to be a lying boy either."

"I'm glad, Bert," Becky spoke quietly. Then she looked at the pile of purple jelly beans. "Shall we just pitch these into the garden?"

"Of course not. I need these to help me remember." Bert scooped up the purple candy and clapped it into his mouth. He chewed rapidly, making horrible faces at his twin all the while.

"But that's only nineteen," Becky said, laughing. "You'll have to eat twenty-one out of the next bag we get."

Bert grimaced and gave a final swallow. Then he said, "As for those other twenty-one jelly beans in the next bag, there just isn't going to be any next bag. I don't think I want to see any more jelly beans forever. And that's no exaggeration."

And Becky believed him.

—Ruth K. Hobbs

Primer Lesson

Look out how you use proud words.
When you let proud words go, it is not easy to call
   them back.
They wear long boots, hard boots; they walk off
   proud; they can't hear you calling—
Look out how you use proud words.   5

–Carl Sandburg

*"B*e not wise in thine own eyes: fear the LORD, *and depart from evil."* Proverbs 3:7

Take It From Me—I Know
Part 1

Becky knew exactly why Chad did what he did—but did she really?

"Bert, Bert, I've found some . . . Mother, where is Bert?" Becky halted, panting, in the middle of the cabin.

Mrs. Baxter had been sitting before the wide screened window of the cabin looking out over the blue waves of the mountains that stretched away to the far horizon. She turned to her **disheveled** daughter. "He left with Chad a while ago to work on their hide-out. What have you been doing?"

Becky flopped on the worn couch. "That's the way it has been ever since we came up here. Chad, Chad, Chad! Bert hasn't done a thing with me after he and Chad got together the first day we came. I'd rather be home than up here in these mountains with nothing to do. I know I'm not going to have any fun at all."

"Don't jump to **conclusions** so soon," Mother advised mildly. "We've been here only three days."

"That's long enough when you're by yourself. Bert will stick with Chad all the rest of the time too. Take it from me—I know."

"Why, what is wrong with you, Becky?" Mother asked in surprise. "You know we are here mainly because Daddy has revival meetings. You were the one who was the most excited about renting this cabin and being with him during the meetings. And you convinced Bert that he could have more fun up here than at Uncle Dave's farm. Didn't I hear you preaching him a sermon about how good it would be for him to **associate** with a mountain boy like Chad and learn a few things?"

Becky's usual dimpled smile broke through the frown as she remembered the lecture she had given her twin brother. "But I wanted him along so we could do things together. And now he is so **engrossed** with Chad that he doesn't do anything but run around with him."

"Didn't they promise to show you their hide-out and let you play in it too, as soon as it was finished?"

"Yes, but what can I do with myself till then?"

"You started a wildflower garden at the Big Rock the very first day we came. Why don't you go and hunt some new flowers?"

"That's just what I've been doing, and I found some bird-foot violets. But I can't get them. They're up among the rocks beside the falls. I tried several times to reach them but kept sliding back down. That's why I'm such a sight. Bert could get them for me in a minute, but where is he? Off with Chad. I might as well not have a brother."

"Don't pity yourself," advised Mother. "I can't blame Bert for wanting to be with Chad. That boy knows the most interesting things about birds and insects and flowers. Didn't they say they are fixing something special for you at the hide-out? That's why they sneak off to themselves. They don't want you to see it until it is finished.

"Bert hasn't forgotten he owns a sister. Remember, he brought you a gift from town just yesterday."

At that, Becky's dimples flashed back and with them her good humor. "Honestly, Mother, it was really funny. You know Bert never in all his life brought me a gift just for anyhow. He was feeling guilty because he hadn't asked me if I wanted to go along to town with him and Chad."

"Are you sure you aren't jumping to conclusions again?" asked Mother.

"Yes, I'm sure," Becky declared, "because Bert practically always asks me to go along with him places like that."

"But three on Slow Girl!" Mother exclaimed. "How would that have looked?"

Becky laughed. "Oh, don't worry. I wouldn't have gone. You won't catch me riding with two boys to town on a poky old mule. That would be too **conspicuous.** But just the same, the pot holders were supposed to be a pacifier. Take it from me—I know."

Becky crossed the cabin and took Bert's gift from the wall above the sink. It was a wrought-iron cat face. Hanging from each cheek was a bright red pot holder.

"It's funny, Mother. For all Chad knows about nature, he had never seen a magnet. Bert had to explain several times that the pot holders stick to the cat face because a little magnetized piece of iron is sewn in one corner of each. He kept feeling them and sticking them on and pulling them off I don't know how many times. Said he'd like to have some to give his grandmother. But, you know, he doesn't have any money to buy pot holders."

"I suppose not," agreed Mother, "but it was nice of him to think of his grandmother. Now, since you are feeling better, how about mixing up a batch of cookies? I promised Angie Higgins to visit her today; so I might as well walk over there before it gets too hot."

"All right," said Becky, hanging up the cat face. "I'll make some of the Crunchy Crisps from the *Mennonite Community Cookbook.*"

"We have no coconut," Mother reminded, "but you can use the black walnuts Chad's grandmother gave us."

In a few minutes Mother started down the hill through the pines, leaving Becky engrossed in cookie making.

An hour and a half later the cookies were finished, laid out neatly on a cloth on the table to cool. Mother had not yet returned, and the cabin suddenly seemed very quiet and lonely.

Wish I knew where Bert and Chad are, Becky thought. *One of these days I feel like sneaking after them and finding out where the hide-out is located. They aren't making anything special for me. They don't want to associate with a girl. That's just their excuse to keep me from tagging along and bothering them.*

"Jumping to conclusions again," Becky seemed to hear her mother's voice. She turned uncomfortably from the thought. It seemed that Mother had to remind her of that bad habit so often. Becky always defended herself when Mother talked to her about it, but deep inside she was beginning to realize what an ugly habit it was.

For a long time Becky had believed that her way of jumping to conclusions was just a sign that she was quicker than anyone else at catching on to people's real motives. She liked to think she was sharp at "seeing through" others.

But recently it had dawned on her that there were getting to be quite a lot of people she didn't like very well, simply because she suspected them of various things.

"I've got to quit jumping to conclusions every time I see a little something that looks suspicious," she decided, tossing the pot holders on the table and putting the last cookie sheet to soak. "It is queer, but every time you judge someone, it's kinda like robbing yourself of a friend, because you can never feel right toward that person as long as you suspect him of some wrong."

Becky spread a cloth over the cookies on the table, then decided to work on her wildflower garden. "Might as well go to the creek and dig up the cardinal flower I saw," she said to herself. "Maybe Bert will get the bird-foot violets for me in the morning."

The Big Rock was on the side of the mountain directly above the cabin. It jutted from the earth like the edge of a giant coin. You could walk out on it and sit, dangling your bare feet into space over the side. From there Becky could see Angie Higgins' cabin in a steep clearing half a mile away. She could see a narrow trail draped like a tan thread over the top of the ridge. She could see the side door of their own cabin and part of the rough stone chimney.

Beneath the Big Rock the sun shone only a little while in the morning. The earth was black and damp. Luxuriant ferns and soft mosses grew there. Even on the hottest days it was cool under the Big Rock. It was there that Becky had started a wildflower garden.

Now she hurried to the creek where she had seen the brilliant flame of a cardinal flower bloom. With one skillful thrust of her shovel, she lifted the entire plant and transferred it to a pail.

Back at the Big Rock she dug a hole and carefully settled the plant into it. The flower should be watered, but Becky's climb from the creek with the pail had been tiring. She decided to rest before going to the house for water. She scrambled up and stretched out on top of the rock.

No sign of Mother in the clearing around Angie Higgins' cabin. No one on the trail across the ridge. Only the harsh scolding of a yellow-breasted chat nearby gave life to the hot afternoon.

Then a small movement below made Becky's half-closed eyes fly open. She saw a boy step quietly to the side door of the cabin. Chad. He rapped, waited a moment, then knocked again. Becky opened her mouth to call to him when, to her astonishment, Chad opened the door and disappeared within.

Becky sat up. She had barely time to catch her breath before Chad reappeared, closed the screen door carefully, and disappeared. But not before Becky had seen that one pocket of his overalls bulged conspicuously.

I thought he was with Bert. What can he want snooping

around the cabin? Then she thought of her cookies spread out on the table. "I'm sure he snitched a handful," she said aloud. "If I had gone for water a minute earlier, I'd have caught him at it."

Becky scrambled to her feet and grabbed the pail. "I know exactly how many there were. Six rows with ten in each row. Take it from me—I know. I had to eat four to make it come out even. Just you wait, Mr. Chad. I'll soon find out how many you took."

—Ruth K. Hobbs

"Thanks be to God, which giveth us the victory through our Lord Jesus Christ."   1 Corinthians 15:57

Take It From Me—I Know
Part 2

Becky had determined to stop accusing others of wrong-doing when she had no proof. But then something happened that really didn't need proof—the evidence was too plain to be ignored.

A moment later Becky entered the cabin. Nothing seemed disturbed. Quickly **depositing** the pail on the table she flipped off the cloth. Then she stood with hands on hips, **baffled.** There were six rows with ten in each row. Chad hadn't touched one cookie.

"Jumping to conclusions again," her conscience barked at her. "Thought you were going to quit that hateful habit of evil surmising."

Slowly Becky gathered the cookies together and put them in the cookie jar. Slowly she took the pail outside to the pump and started filling it with water. Slowly she trudged to the Big Rock and watered the drooping cardinal flower. Then she sat down to think.

"How could I?" she whispered **contritely** to herself. "Just after I had vowed to stop accusing people falsely."

Becky received only small comfort from remembering that no one had heard her accuse Chad. She knew if someone had been with her, she would have accused him just the same.

Anyway, the sin was in her surmising evil of Chad, not in someone else's knowing about it. Calling her bad habit a sin was bitter medicine for Becky to swallow.

"But calling it something else besides sin won't *make* it something else," she decided.

After coming to that conclusion, Becky stood up. "This *will* be the last time," she declared solemnly. "Rebecca Baxter, today you have stopped judging people's motives and actions. You have stopped jumping to conclusions." Then Becky closed her eyes a moment and asked the Lord to forgive her. She asked Him to give her love so she would want to think good of others. "And please Lord," she prayed, "help me recognize and have victory over my next temptation."

Then she skipped down to the cabin. Her happiness continued even when Bert, at the supper table, said he couldn't get the violets until he and Chad had finished the hide-out.

For the first time, Becky thought about how it must be for Bert not to have a brother—to have only his sister to play with. No wonder he wanted to spend every possible moment with his friend. And Chad, living alone on the mountain with his grandmother, must appreciate Bert's companionship even more.

As far as her wildflower garden was concerned, she didn't have very much in it anyway. If Mother and Daddy bought the cabin, as they were talking of doing, she would have plenty of time to work on the garden.

At breakfast the next morning, Mother set the scrambled eggs on the table, holding the plate with the corner of her apron. "Becky, where are your new pot holders?"

Becky looked over the rim of her milk glass. "I don't know. Aren't they on the cat face?"

"No. I couldn't find them last evening either."

"I used them yesterday when I made the cookies."

"What did you do with them? Did you hang them up?"

"I can't remember whether I did or not."

"Think a little."

Becky frowned thoughtfully. "I put my baking things in the sink to soak, then covered the cookies with a tea towel. Can't remember hanging the pot holders up. Guess I just left them on the table."

Mother sighed. "You've got to think harder than that, Becky. The cabin is too small to hide two red pot holders. I've looked high and low. They simply are not in the house. You must have done something with them. You were the only one here."

"I know," she admitted in a baffled tone, "but . . ." Becky suddenly stopped. She *wasn't* the only one who had been in the cabin yesterday afternoon. So that's what Chad had sneaked into the house for! Well, if he thought he could get by with stealing! Even if it was for his grandmother.

Then Becky remembered. She remembered the prayer she had prayed at the Big Rock. She remembered the promise she had made to God.

But this was too obvious. The pot holders with the magnets had fascinated Chad from the first. He had practically said he wished he had them. Maybe he thought it wasn't wrong if he took them to give to his grandmother.

"But you didn't see him take them," Becky's conscience reminded her.

"They were here when I left," she argued. "And although I didn't notice them when I came in to check on those cookies, Mother came home soon afterward and couldn't find them. Chad was the only one in the cabin during that time."

Becky rolled the arguments around in her mind. Then this thought came: *You promised God not to accuse people of things you couldn't prove. How can you expect Him to help you if you deliberately break your promise?*

Suddenly she understood. She was being tempted. It was the first time Becky remembered actually recognizing a temptation while she was facing it. And she wasn't going to yield. She certainly wasn't.

"I'm keeping my promise, Lord," she whispered. "I'm not even going to *think* that Chad took the pot holders."

Becky stood and began stacking the breakfast dishes. As she deposited them in the sink, she said, "I haven't any idea what I did with them, Mother. But they will turn up, I'm sure." Becky suddenly felt intensely happy again.

The days passed and the red pot holders did not show up. Try as they might, none of the other Baxters could offer a solution to the mystery. The pot holders had simply dropped out of sight.

"It is not that they are so valuable," Mother said over and over again, "but it is so baffling for them to disappear like that."

Becky could have suggested an answer, but she never

246

hinted at what she had seen, for she refused to believe Chad had stolen the pot holders.

This knowledge gave her the deepest satisfaction. It proved she truly had won the victory. It was a wonderful feeling.

In addition to that, she realized she didn't care if she never saw the pot holders again. *Nothing else really matters when you know you are having victory over sin,* she thought, marveling at the grown-up discovery.

"Becky, we finished the hide-out this morning," announced Bert at the dinner table one day. "I can get those violets for you this afternoon."

"Good. I'm finished eating. I'll get the pail and shovel right now. Where are they, Mother?" Becky jumped up from the table.

"The shovel is standing in the chimney corner, but I don't know where the pail is," replied Mother.

A quick search around the cabin proved fruitless. "Maybe I left it at the Big Rock when I planted that cardinal flower," Becky said. "Didn't realize I hadn't been up there since then. May as well run up and look."

A few minutes later Bert and Mother were startled to see a disheveled Becky flying down the hill. She burst through the cabin door. In one hand she swung the pail, in the other waved the missing red pot holders.

"Mother! Bert! The pot holders. He didn't do it. I knew all the time he didn't. They were stuck on the bottom of the pail. I carried them to the Big Rock myself. Oh, I'm so glad!"

"What are you talking about? Who didn't do what? Calm

down a little and explain what you mean," Mother suggested, recovering from her surprise at seeing the long-lost pot holders.

Becky got a second breath and told her story. She omitted several details for reasons of her own and hoped Mother wouldn't notice that she had failed to answer her second question.

"You remember the day the pot holders disappeared, you had gone to visit Angie Higgins. I baked cookies and left them on the table to cool. I must have left the pot holders there too. Then I transplanted that cardinal flower to my garden at the Big Rock. When I came to the house with the pail for water, I decided to put the cookies away. I set the pail on the table, evidently on top of the pot holders. Of course they stuck on the bottom, and I carried them to the Big Rock and forgot to bring the pail back to the cabin."

"Well, if that doesn't beat all!" exclaimed Mother.

"Whew, am I ever glad they are found!" breathed Bert.

Becky wondered at the tone of relief in her twin's voice, and a few minutes later as they started out for the violets, she learned the reason.

"You thought Chad had taken the pot holders, didn't you?" Bert asked.

"No, I didn't," Becky answered, happy that she could truthfully deny the charge. "Did you?"

"Well, I didn't know," Bert confessed. "I had sent Chad to the cabin that day for some twine. I would have come myself. Only I was . . . Never mind what I was doing," Bert interrupted himself and grinned. "It just suited better for Chad to come. I told him if no one answered his knock to go on in and get the twine ball from the sink drawer. When those pot holders disappeared the same afternoon, and I knew the cabin had been empty when he got the twine, it looked mighty suspicious. I couldn't believe Chad would steal, yet there seemed no other explanation for the mystery. But it wasn't fair to accuse him just on circumstantial evidence."

"That's right, and what's more, it wouldn't be Christian either," declared Becky positively. "Take it from me—I know."

—Ruth K. Hobbs

"Hereby perceive we the love of God, because he laid down his life for us: and we ought to lay down our lives for the brethren."

1 John 3:16

I Still Think It Was a Miracle
Part 1

The teacher had hinted that if Jerry flunked social studies he might have to repeat the whole grade next year. Jerry desperately wished for more time to study in the evenings. But he knew of no way to get that. Right now, what he really needed was a miracle.

"I sure hope we can figure out who the right character is," Jerry exclaimed, boring into his lunch bag for the cookies at the bottom. "I'm in **desperate** need of a couple of big, fat A's to elevate my grade in social studies or I'm going to flunk it for sure."

The other eighth graders settled on the wall along the school drive and immediately began chattering about their latest assignment—the last before Christmas vacation.

"I can't see what is so hard about choosing which Bible character in the Christmas story showed the true Christmas spirit," declared Leon. "Simple matter of **elimination.** Let's list who it *wasn't,* and the rest will be easy."

"It couldn't have been Caesar Augustus. All he did was

issue that decree about taxes."

"We can eliminate Herod too. Killing all those babies didn't show such a great Christmas spirit."

"The scribes and Pharisees. They didn't do anything outstanding."

"I don't think it was even Jesus," Julia volunteered slowly.

"Well, that's who I thought it likely was," Jerry exclaimed. "He is the One Christmas is all about."

"That's true in a way. But He came to die, and at this point in His life He didn't do anything but be born. Mr. Ross said we should study what the characters in the story did or said. Jesus didn't do or say anything."

"Well then, who does that leave us to choose from?" demanded Matt.

"The angels."

"The shepherds."

"Mary and Joseph."

"The wise men."

"That's still five people," admitted Leon **ruefully.** "Maybe it won't be as easy as I thought."

"The purpose of this project," the teacher had said, "is for you to discover the true spirit of Christmas, and to see if it brings happiness to you. Here's what I want you to do:

"First, read the Christmas story from Matthew and Luke and list all the characters mentioned. As you read, think carefully about what each person did or said and decide which showed the best and truest Christmas spirit.

"Then plan a project in which you do something for

someone else that demonstrates the same spirit."

Hands began going up over the room but Mr. Ross ignored them. "And finally, make a report telling why you chose your character and explaining what your project was." A few groans were also ignored. "Your report will be due the first social studies period after Christmas vacation. That will be the last period on Monday after New Year's Day. Now, have you any questions?"

"How long does the report have to be?"

"Can it be an oral report?"

"May we work together if our project takes more than one person?"

"What if we all decide on the same character and try to do the same thing?"

"May we tell each other what character we chose?"

"Can our parents help if we need grown-ups to do the projects?"

Mr. Ross waited until the questions stopped, then answered, "Your reports may be oral or written. They should be long enough to show that you discovered the true spirit of Christmas and demonstrated it plainly to someone else. You may talk about the project to anyone you please and get any-one you need to help you. But this is to be a personal project. Pick the character *you* think showed the true Christmas spirit and don't let yourself be influenced unduly by what your classmates decide."

"What if we don't choose the right character but plan a nice project and give a good report?" asked Jerry.

"I thought about that," replied Mr. Ross, "and I decided to

grade you in four areas. Choosing the right character will count one hundred points. A well-planned and executed project will earn you a hundred more. If you have a good report, that will be another hundred points. And if your spirit throughout the assignment passes my inspection, you will be given another hundred points."

Jerry's hand shot up. "You mean we could earn four A's if we did everything perfectly?"

The teacher nodded.

"Oh, great! But I'm not sure what you mean by that last point about our 'spirit throughout the assignment.'"

"Me either."

"Neither am I."

"Nor I."

Again Mr. Ross waited till the room was absolutely quiet. Then he spoke seriously, "Class, I didn't plan this project simply to give you something to work on during vacation. You are old enough to stop thinking of Christmas as a time for getting presents, or for enjoying a lot of good things to eat."

"As I said in the beginning, the purpose is for you to experience the true Christmas spirit yourself. Let's say you did choose the right story character, and planned a good project and wrote a good report. If you didn't catch the true spirit of Christmas yourself, in my opinion, you have failed."

"I still don't get it," Leon protested.

"Let me illustrate. Suppose you decide the wise men showed the true Christmas spirit—I'm not saying they did. I'm just using them as an example. So you plan to give gifts to someone like the wise men did. You even give to people who cannot give something in return any more than Baby Jesus could. But suppose I hear you griping, or perhaps bragging, about how much money you spent for those gifts. Maybe you act **disgruntled** because you didn't get the enthusiastic thanks you thought you deserved. You might act disappointed because you gave more than you got, or grumble because you didn't have time to do everything you had planned during this vacation. That would show me you had completely failed to catch the true spirit of giving. And you would get zero on that part of the assignment. Understand?"

Yes, they had finally understood. Now the big question was, which character in the Christmas story showed the true Christmas spirit?

"I think it was the wise men," declared Leon. "Giving is always the main idea around Christmastime—even worldly people know that. Mr. Ross said he used the wise men only as an example. But I think he was just trying to throw us off the track."

"Well, I'm sure it *wasn't* them," said Julia, just as emphatically. "Choosing the right character is the most important part of the assignment. He wouldn't have given us any hints like that."

Then Sue spoke up. "I think the angels played a more important part than we think. They brought the news of Christ's birth to the world. The first thing God did that night was to send the angels to earth with the Good News. And practically the last thing Jesus told His disciples was to go into the world and tell the Good News. All the gift-giving you see every

Christmas has nothing to do with the spirit God wants us to have."

"It seems to me that every Christmas we hear a lot of talk about the Christmas spirit and what it is," said Matt. "Here we are wondering again this year. The very fact that we are arguing about it now shows me it probably isn't any of the characters we always think about first. Couldn't it have been Joseph? God talked to him in dreams more often than anyone I know of. And Joseph always obeyed whatever God told him to do. Isn't doing the will of God the real Christmas spirit? That's what Jesus did when He came to earth. That's what the angels did when they appeared to the shepherds. That's what the wise men did when they followed the star. Why couldn't obedience be the true Christmas spirit?"

"I disagree," stated Henry in a tone of finality. "I think the true spirit of Christmas is love. Jesus came because He loved us, and God so loved the world that He gave His Son. The whole Bible, not just the Christmas story, is the story of the love of God and Jesus."

"But God wasn't one of the characters in the Christmas account," Sue pointed out. "And Jesus didn't do anything in the story."

"As long as we are arguing, I think I could make out a pretty good case for the shepherds," said Tina. "The Christmas spirit could be faith. That's what the shepherds showed. Imagine leaving their sheep out there in the country for the wolves to gobble up, and going into Bethlehem in the middle of the night. And they didn't have any flashlights or streetlights. They must have had a lot of faith in what the angels told them.

The only clue they had was that Jesus was in a manger wrapped in swaddling clothes. You think they knocked on people's doors and asked permission to go out to their barn and look into their manger for a newborn baby? Fancy getting people out of bed with such a tale! Or did they just go snooping around in stables without asking permission? Either way would have taken more faith than I would have had. Without faith it is impossible to please God, so I think the true Christmas spirit could be faith just as well as obedience or love."

The students laughed, then Leon asked, "Jerry, you haven't said a word. Who do you think showed the true Christmas spirit?"

"Mr. Ross said we shouldn't let ourselves be influenced by other people's opinions. To tell the truth, I've not been listening much to all your gabbing. All I've been thinking is that if I can make four A's, I won't flunk social studies."

"Gabbing seems to be all we have accomplished," Leon declared, jumping from the wall and brushing crumbs from his trousers. He spread his hand and counted off on his fingers. "Look, one of us thinks it was the wise men. One thinks it was the shepherds. Another has voted for Joseph, and another for the angels. Giving, obedience, faith, love, telling others the Good News—that's four people and five things that have been suggested. Only one can be right, which means most of us are wrong. We haven't settled a thing and vacation begins tomorrow."

"We'll just have to do as Mr. Ross said," Jerry concluded as they all headed for the schoolhouse. "Each decide for himself.

One thing is certain, I've got to hit upon the right character or there are going to be some unfortunate circumstances occurring on my next report card."

After getting off the bus that evening and starting the mile-long walk up the lane, Jerry began thinking seriously. His light-hearted comments about his social studies grades were more true than his classmates realized. Likely they had forgotten he had repeated second grade. And they surely never suspected how close he had come to failing several years since.

Schoolwork had always been hard for him. He would have had a better chance if his father were living and he had evenings for homework like the other students. As it was, helping his mother on their little country place after she got home from work left no time for schoolwork. More than that, he often helped his grandparents who lived across the yard. Every Saturday he went with Grandpa to market to help him set up his stand where he sold the baked goods Grandma made on Friday.

Jerry's mind spun back to his social studies problem. The way he had it figured after talking with Mr. Ross several weeks ago, if he didn't jack up that social studies grade, he might not pass this year.

Could this assignment be the answer to his recent, rather desperate prayers? Four A's without having to read any chapters in the text. Without having to look up a dozen unpronounceable words and trying to figure out what they meant in the lesson. Without having to hunt answers to any questions. Without having to do any research in the library. Four A's that he could earn during vacation without a lick of study! It surely was an answer to prayer.

And with that assurance Jerry suddenly relaxed. "Then You will help me figure out who the right character is," he said out loud to the Lord. "All that talk at noon today left everyone so mixed up that I may as well forget it. Somehow I still think it must be Jesus. Without Him, there wouldn't even be a Christmas. True, Jesus didn't *do* anything on the first Christmas night, but—but—" Suddenly the truth hit him. That was it! The simple wonderful fact of His *being* there in that manger was what Christmas was all about. The *giving of Himself!* That was the spirit of Christmas!

Jerry felt like dancing a jig. "Thank You. Oh, thank You, Lord. There's one A all sewed up. Now for the project. How can I give myself to someone?"

Jerry walked slower. Fragments of several verses ran through his busy mind. "Jesus came to save sinners"; "Who gave himself a ransom for all." Of course, he couldn't give himself a ransom for sinners as Jesus did, but couldn't he somehow give himself to sinners in a different way? Were there any sinners he had contact with? Certainly no one at home or school or church. Even their nearest neighbors, three miles away, were Christians from their own church.

The only sinners he really ever talked to much were people at market on Saturdays. At least he guessed they were sinners. Then just like that, the idea for his project popped into his mind almost full grown.

The Christmas and New Year's season was a hectic time at market. Lots of people could use his help. After Grandpa's produce was carried in and arranged, Grandpa could easily take care of the customers himself. In fact, market day was the highlight of Grandpa's week, and he preferred waiting on the customers himself. Jerry would be free to help anyone he pleased.

That's what his project would be. He would give himself as a helper to different people in the market.

Old Mr. Broddus for example: His stall was beside Grandpa's and he always became flustered when two or three customers stopped at his stand at the same time. There would be a number of ways he could make it easier for Mr. Broddus.

Then there was Mrs. Vashinsky on the other side. She had trouble with English and often couldn't understand what customers wanted. "I could keep my ear cocked that way and come to her rescue when she gets stuck, instead of expecting Grandpa to help her out."

And the Ellroy sisters always took forever to carry in their things. "I could get them set up by myself faster than both of them put together," he planned happily. Another minute and Jerry had thought of enough people he could volunteer to help at market to keep him busy for the three Saturdays left before the end of Christmas vacation.

"And there is A number two," he said with satisfaction.

He had already decided to give an oral report. Talking came easy with him. Writing reports was work, and he usually didn't make the best grades in written work. Why **jeopardize** that third A by straining his shaky knowledge of outlining, grammar, sentence structure, and paragraphing—not to mention his handwriting—as would be required in a written report? A lively explanation and description of his encounters with the folks he had helped at market should assure him of that third A.

The fourth A posed no problem. He would have no trouble catching the spirit of giving himself to others. Already he could hardly wait to begin. Now Jerry hurried. Those four A's were as good as won. Wait till he told his mother!

The moment he rounded the last bend and came within sight of the house, he noticed the empty carport. "She must have had to work late," he mused. Usually Mother arrived before he got home from school. Jerry turned toward his grandparent's little cottage among the pines. Mother always phoned Grandma when she couldn't make it home on time.

Grandpa's pickup was in the garage but no one answered Jerry's knock nor his call when he stuck his head in the door and hollered, "Grandma."

Crossing the yard to his own house, Jerry couldn't at first explain the feeling of uneasiness that enveloped him. Then it struck him. Friday afternoons his spry little grandma was always scurrying around her kitchen, up to her ears in making things for market. Where, oh, where was she? What could have happened to call her away on Friday?

He saw the sheet of paper taped to the refrigerator the moment he entered the kitchen. His mother's usually neat handwriting was an almost **illegible** scrawl. "G'ma—stroke. Her and G'pa to hosp. Will call or come soon."

Jerry numbly changed clothes and went about his chores. It wasn't until he was nearly finished gathering Grandpa's eggs, that through his whirling fears about Grandma another thought smote him. With Grandma in the hospital there would be no going to the market tomorrow. Maybe not even next

Saturday or the next. Jerry stood still and watched four A's disappear into the dusty atmosphere of the henhouse.

—Ruth K. Hobbs

*Do you think Jerry's grandmother had nephews that felt
about her the way this poet felt about his Aunt Mary?*

Out to Old Aunt Mary's

Wasn't it pleasant, O brother mine,
In those old days of the lost sunshine
   Of youth—when the Saturday's chores were through,
   And the "Sunday's wood" in the kitchen, too,
   And we went visiting, "me and you,"
      Out to Old Aunt Mary's?

It all comes back so clear today!
Though I am as bald as you are gray—
   Out by the barn lot and down the lane
   We patter along in the dust again,
   As light as the tips of the drops of rain,
      Out to Old Aunt Mary's!

We cross the pasture, and through the wood,
Where the old gray snag of the poplar stood,
   Where the hammering red-heads hopped awry,
   And the buzzard "raised" in the clearing sky
   And lolled and circled, as we went by
      Out to Old Aunt Mary's.

And then in the dust of the road again;
And the teams we met, and the countrymen;
   And the long highway, with sunshine spread
   As thick as butter on country bread,
   Our cares behind, and our hearts ahead
      Out to Old Aunt Mary's.

Why, I see her now in the open door
Where the little gourds grew up the sides and o'er
   The clapboard roof!—And her face—ah, me!
   Wasn't it good for a boy to see—
   And wasn't it good for a boy to be
      Out to Old Aunt Mary's?

And, O my brother, so far away,
This is to tell you—she waits *today*
   To welcome us:—Aunt Mary fell
   Asleep this morning, whispering, "Tell
   The boys to come." . . . And all is well
      Out to Old Aunt Mary's.

                     – James Whitcomb Riley

"Cast thy burden upon the LORD, and he shall sustain thee."

Psalm 55:22

I Still Think It Was a Miracle
Part 2

The social studies assignment was a plain miraculous answer to Jerry's desperate prayer. But then it had vanished—as instantly as it had appeared. Now what could Jerry do?

It was after dark before Mother brought Grandpa home. When the lights shone from the windows across the yard, Jerry ran over. Grandpa had gone to his bedroom and closed the door. As Jerry helped Mother put away the baking things Grandma had been using that morning, she told him all that had happened since Grandpa had called her at work. "Now she is lying in the hospital bed not knowing anything or anyone. The doctors say it will likely be only a short time until she goes to be with the Lord.

"Now, dear, I am going to make you a bed here on the couch. Grandpa didn't want to sleep at our place, but I think someone should be here with him. Do you mind? I must go and call Uncle Teddy and Uncle Ralph and Aunt Ella."

"No, Mother. I'll do anything for Grandpa," said Jerry,

huskily, swiping at his eyes with the back of his hand. "Just go on. I'll be all right."

The doctors were right. Grandma never returned to the little house among the pines. The day before Christmas they laid her body to rest in the church cemetery.

After the funeral Uncle Ralph and Uncle Teddy both begged Grandpa to go home with them at least for a while—maybe till spring. Aunt Ella said she had an empty house trailer in her yard that Grandpa could move into; but he shook his head. "I'll have to get used to the place without Grandma sometime. It will be best to begin now. Won't be any easier later."

So all the relatives had gone home.

Grandpa insisted that Mother go back to her job. "I know you need the money. I'll have Jerry and we will make out fine."

So on Monday Mother had gone to work and only then did Jerry remember that Christmas had come and gone and he had never once thought about what day it was. He was glad there was still a week of vacation left, for he could hardly bear to think of going back to school and leaving Grandpa alone.

"Try to keep Grandpa busy and talking," Mother had said to him that first morning before she left for work.

"All right, but what are we going to do after I start back to school?" asked Jerry. "He'll be alone all day till you get home. He doesn't even have market to look forward to on Saturdays anymore."

"I've been thinking of that too," Mother had replied, "and I'm working on an idea, so if you can see him through this week yet, maybe things will change after that. And Jerry," she

265

continued, laying her hand on his shoulder, "remember I'm praying for you all the time during the day. You know God really can solve all your problems. Turn them over to Him. Don't wrestle with them all by yourself."

Jerry turned away unable to reply. Being responsible for Grandpa all week weighed heavily on his mind. Mother's prayers would help; but she didn't know about his social studies problem. He hadn't had time to tell her, and now he wasn't going to worry her with anything else.

And so began the longest and most **stressful** week Jerry ever remembered. A dozen times a day he would find Grandpa standing in the middle of a job looking off into the distance or sitting in his rocker staring at the floor. And it was his job to keep Grandpa working and talking!

Every night before he fell asleep, he tried to plan what they could do the next day—jobs that he and Grandpa could work at together—jobs that would take a long time.

On Monday they cleaned the henhouse, scattering the litter on the garden. Then they drove to town and got new shavings for the floor and the nests. Jerry even got Grandpa to wash the inside of the windows while he washed the outside, though he nearly froze his hands doing it.

On Tuesday they cleaned out the garage and the basement, carting the junk off to the county dump.

On Wednesday he and Grandpa fixed the fence around the pasture and the garden, checking every post and every board. It was a relief when Grandpa decided to replace several posts and some of the boards. That job took them till almost supper time.

Thursday dawned mild and sunny, and at Jerry's suggestion Grandpa cranked up his tractor and plowed under the chicken manure they had spread on the garden. Then they raked the yard and flower beds of the last of the leaves and tree branches that had blown down.

On Friday a cold rain fell. That meant spending the day indoors. The memory of other Fridays in Grandma's cheery kitchen, with her bustling around at her baking, was almost too much for Jerry. But he put those thoughts aside and asked, "Shall we do the Saturday cleaning today, Grandpa? Then tomorrow we could drive in to the market and see everyone again. Would you like that?"

Grandpa looked at Jerry with tears in his eyes. "Jerry, I know your mom told you to keep me busy this week. You've really kept me on the jump, and it has been a big help. Yes, I would like to go to market tomorrow. I'll really miss going to market. But that's something else that is over forever, I guess. I would like to go back and tell everyone good-bye."

That's the way the week had dragged by. Jerry had been so occupied with Grandpa that only at night did he have time to wrestle with the social studies assignment due the last period on Monday. Perhaps Mr. Ross would let him do his project later. But then, what could he do since the market project had fallen through? Why had God handed him those four A's so plainly, only to snatch them away again? That question was an even heavier burden than his responsibility for Grandpa. But no answer had come, and no idea of how to **salvage** his social studies grade—until Friday evening at supper. Jerry was so weary he almost dozed off at the table. Then he heard Mother say, "Well, Father, I've quit my job."

He jerked awake and he and Grandpa both stared.

"Aw, Mindy, you didn't have to do that. Don't you think I'm old enough to stay by myself during the day?"

Grandpa's attempt at a joke made Jerry feel good. It sounded like Grandpa again.

"I've decided to take over Grandma's market baking. With Jerry to help, we can bake a lot more than Grandma did. And I plan to start making jelly and candy too. In the spring we will put out garden things for market. Then we could go two or three days a week. If you want to be responsible for the selling end of things, I'm sure we will do all right."

The happy moisture in Grandpa's eyes was all the answer Mother needed.

A glimmer of hope sprang up in Jerry's heart. If he had even one day at market, maybe he could help enough people to be able to make some kind of report on Monday. He sat up straighter and tried to speak casually. "Do you think it's too late to get some things together to sell at market tomorrow, Mother? Grandpa and I planned to go in to say good-bye. We could stay longer if we had something to sell."

"Well, now we won't need to go in tomorrow," Grandpa interrupted happily. "Since I'll be going back like usual, we can just skip one more market day and get back to business next Saturday."

"I'll need most of next week to learn how Grandma did things," Mother added. "Anyway, Jerry, you look about ready to drop. You were almost asleep a minute ago. Why don't you go on upstairs and sleep in your own bed tonight? Tomorrow take the day off and do as you please. You've had a hard week. School starts Monday and you haven't had any vacation at all."

"Yes, he's just about worn himself to a frazzle looking after me," Grandpa said with a tremble in his voice. "I don't know how I'd have made it this first week if it hadn't been for Jerry. But now if I can keep on going to market, I'll have work to do and something to look forward to every week. I'm just going to keep hanging onto the Lord and He'll make everything come out all right."

Jerry said good night and went upstairs. He sank wearily onto the edge of his bed and began to untie his shoes. Mother's words had lifted the heavy burden of Grandpa from his tired shoulders. He hadn't realized until now what a strain he had been under. He was almost too exhausted to undress.

Yes, that burden was gone, but not the problem at school. He had failed in his last attempt to do that social studies assignment before Monday. There just wasn't anything else to try. It would take a miracle to change things now.

True, he would get one A for choosing the right character. He was sure of that. But what good would one A do him? He would get zero in the other three parts of the assignment. Even he, poor as he was in math, could figure in his head the average of three zeros and one hundred. Mechanically he finished getting ready for bed.

Then Grandpa's words swept into his mind. *I'm going to keep hanging onto the Lord. He'll make everything come out all right.*

Well, that's what I'm going to do, Jerry resolved. *I'm too tired to think any more. I've done what I could, Lord, so I'll just turn it all over to You. Anyway, how important is flunking social studies or even failing eighth grade, compared to losing Grandma?*

With that decision, another weight dropped from Jerry's shoulders. He curled up in bed, pulled the blanket over his ear, and sank into dreamless sleep for the first time in two weeks.

On Monday morning as he walked down the lane to meet the bus, Jerry planned what he would do when Mr. Ross called on him in social studies. "First, I'll explain why I chose Jesus as the character who showed the true spirit of Christmas. Then I'll just say that because Grandma died, I couldn't do the project I had planned. I'll not even tell them how busy I was with Grandpa. I don't want anybody to pity me."

The last period of the day finally rolled around. Mr. Ross called for the reports one by one. The angels, the shepherds, Joseph, and the wise men—every character they had discussed that day before vacation had been chosen by one or more of the students. The projects they reported were varied and interesting. Everyone seemed to have enjoyed the assignment.

Mr. Ross called on Jerry last. He walked to the front of the room and gave the little speech he had planned. As he sat down, Jerry could almost feel the warm sympathy of his classmates flowing around him. All of them had been to Grandma's funeral and understood why he hadn't been able to do the assignment.

Leon raised his hand. "Mr. Ross, couldn't you give Jerry some extra time to do his project?"

"Well—" A long pause. Then Mr. Ross said, "How about

taking up that question after class? If everyone agrees to your suggestion, Leon, I'll consider that possibility. Right now, I want to discuss some of your projects so you will understand more clearly the grades I will be giving you.

"You'll be glad to know that I'm giving each of you a hundred for your attitudes toward the assignment. Obviously you have put your hearts into it and enjoyed your projects.

"For the most part your reports were pretty good. However," here Mr. Ross paused and smiled kindly, "only one of you selected the right character. Jerry, will you tell us again why you chose Jesus?"

"I thought the true spirit of Christmas was not just giving gifts as the wise men did, but giving *yourself* as Jesus did. Although He didn't do or say anything on that first Christmas day, His *being* there in the manger showed He truly gave Himself. That's what I thought, anyhow."

Mr. Ross nodded, then said, "Now will you tell us about the project you had planned?"

So Jerry explained how he had wanted to go to market with Grandpa and give himself as a helper to anyone who needed him.

"One more question: What did you do all last week after your grandmother's funeral?"

"You mean what I did every day?"

"Well, yes, as much as you can remember."

And Jerry began, "Mother said I was supposed to try to keep Grandpa occupied while she was at work so that he wouldn't just be sitting around thinking about Grandma. So that's what I tried to do." Then he launched into a day-by-day rehearsal of that long, nerve-racking week.

"I see you were quite busy," said Mr. Ross when he finished. "Too bad you had to waste all that time when you could have been working on your social studies assignment. Four A's would have done quite a bit for your grade, you know."

Jerry looked up in surprise. That remark did not sound like Mr. Ross at all. "No, Mr. Ross," he said quietly. "That's not the way I felt about it at all. 'Course, flunking social studies isn't fun, but I *wanted* to help Grandpa. I'd have done more than that for him, grades or no grades."

At that Mr. Ross stood up behind his desk. "That's all I wanted to hear you say, Jerry." He turned to the class. "It's nearly bell time. If you think over the requirements of the assignment and consider what Jerry has just told us, I am sure you'll agree that he is the only one who deserves an A in all four parts of the assignment."

He smiled at Jerry's dumbfounded look. "Yes, Jerry, you chose the right character and picked the right Christmas spirit. I gave you one A for that. Though you didn't knowingly plan to, you gave yourself to your grandpa all week in a beautiful expression of that spirit. That got you the second A. Your description of how you spent last week was an excellent oral report—A number three. I apologize for making that heartless remark a minute ago, but I needed to make sure of your attitude. Your answer earned you the fourth A."

Someone started to clap, and the dismissal bell shrilled in the middle of the roar that went up from Jerry's classmates. Eighth grade headed for the door.

"Come on, old pal," Leon clapped Jerry on the shoulder.

"Collect your wits or you'll miss the bus. Don't let those four A's go to your head," and out he went.

But Jerry turned to the teacher's desk. "Mr. Ross, I just want to thank you for the—the—the miracle."

"It wasn't really a miracle, Jerry," replied his teacher. "Giving yourself to others—the true spirit of Christmas—has its own built-in rewards. Sometimes those rewards are great, sometimes they are small. But they are always there. That's the way God planned it."

The bus driver tooted his horn and Jerry turned to go. "I still think it was a miracle," he said, "one I hope I'll never forget."

– Ruth K. Hobbs

Of Giving

Not what you Get, but what you Give
Is that which proves your Right to Live.

–Arthur Guiterman

Glossary

In your reader, new words are in boldfaced type. The root word of every boldfaced word is in the glossary. With each word you will find the pronunciation and definition. The definition is for the way the word is used in the reader story, though it may have other definitions. The sentence in *italic type* shows how the word is used.

abrupt (ə brəpt´) – sudden and unexpected. *The car came to an abrupt stop.* 192

absorb (əb zȯrb´) – to suck up; to take up the attention of. *His mind absorbed every word the teacher said.* 99

abstinence (ab´ stə nənts) – doing without something for a certain length of time. *Abstinence is the best way to keep from becoming addicted to strong drink.* 125

accommodations (ə käm´ ə dā´ shənz) – shelter, food, and lodging, as at a hotel. *We traveled until dark; then searched for accommodations for the night.* 147

adequate (ad´ i kwət) – enough; sufficient. *The settlers worked hard to lay by an adequate supply of food for the winter.* 156

adjoin (əd jȯin´) – to be next to. *Dad's office adjoins my room.* 80

admonish (ad män´ ish) – to warn or advise. *Mom admonished Caleb to drive more slowly.* 10

alternate (ȯl´ tər nət) – happening by turns. *The American flag has alternate stripes of red and white.* 9

anchor (ang´ kər) – a heavy weight attached to a boat or ship by a long cable. It has hooks on it that, when thrown overboard, dig into the bottom of the sea and hold the ship in place. *The ship's anchor weighed several hundred pounds.* 126

ancient (ān´ shənt) – very old. *I would like to visit some of the ancient castles in Scotland.* 70

applicant (ap´ li kənt) – a person who asks, or applies, for something, especially a job. *There were three applicants for the position of secretary.* 79

apprehensive (ap´ ri hen´ siv) – full of worry or fear about something that might happen. *Gloria felt apprehensive about the exam coming up.* 216

associate (ə sō´ shē āt´) – to join together; to do things with or be friends with. *Jeremy associates with the other boys from church a lot.* 237

aurora (ə ror′ ə) – a display of natural light in the night sky. It occurs mainly near the polar regions. The lights can be various colors. *The nice thing about living in Alberta is being able to see the aurora on some nights.* 17

baffled (baf′ əld) – puzzled or confused; bewildered. *Who was stealing the corn? Everyone was baffled until we saw raccoon tracks in the field.* 243

befall (bi fol′) – to happen to. *We all wondered what had befallen the messenger.* 51

bellows (bel′ ōz) – a device that blows out a stream of air when its sides are squeezed together, used especially to make a fire burn hotter. *The blacksmith's apprentice used a bellows to keep the fire going strong.* 116

blunder (blən′ dər) – to move clumsily. *We could hear the bear blundering about in the underbrush.* 170

brine (brīn) – salt water. *Mom made a brine to soak the pickles in.* 33

bustle (bəs′ əl) – to hurry busily. *Susanna bustled about the kitchen importantly, pleased to be making supper.* 58

butte (byüt) – a high narrow hill with steep sides and a small flat top. *There are many mesas and buttes in the western United States.* 202

calculate (kal′ kyə lāt′) – to figure out by using math; to estimate. *If I calculated right, there should be two cups of cocoa for everyone.* 60

carcass (kär′ kəs) – the body of a dead animal. *Several vultures were feeding on the deer carcass beside the road.* 168

cavort (kə vort′) – to prance and caper playfully. *The lambs, giddy and full of life, cavorted crazily in the pasture.* 135

circulation (sər′ kyə lā′ shən) – the movement of blood through the veins. *Don't tie that string so tightly around your finger; you'll cut off the circulation.* 20

circumstance (sər′ kəm stants′) – an event or happening. *There were several unusual circumstances at the time of Jesus' birth.* 59

cobble (käb′ əl) – round stone used for paving a street. *The people's shoes clattered on the cobbles of the little street.* 34

commence (kə ments′) – to begin. *Hurry—the bell is commencing to ring!* 14

Pronunciation Key: /ə/ but; /ä/ top; /yü/ use; /ər/ mother; /th/ thick; /<u>th</u>/ this; /or/ corn; /ü/ boot; /u̇/ foot; /o/ lost; /oi/ coin, toy; /är/ star; /au̇/ out; /zh/ measure; /ir/ deer; /er/ bear

conceal (kən sēl′) – to hide. *Nat concealed the candy so his brother wouldn't find it.* 194

conclusion (kən klü′ zhən) – an opinion arrived at by careful thinking. *"You've spent a lot of time thinking about this problem; what is your conclusion?"* 236

congenial (kən jēn′ yəl) – pleasant and kind. *Miss Kurtz greeted us with a congenial smile.* 201

conspicuous (kən spik′ yə wəs) – very noticeable; attracting attention. *Shana felt conspicuous in her Sunday dress when the other girls were dressed for chores.* 238

consternation (kän′ stər nā′ shən) – amazement and dismay. *When the girls realized their predicament, they stared at each other in consternation.* 8

contrite (kən trīt′) – sorry for a sin or mistake. *Sharon apologized contritely for helping spread the false story.* 243

deem (dēm) – to think, consider, or believe. *Dad deemed it best to wait until the roads were cleared before leaving.* 125

deposit (di päz′ ət) – to put or place something. *He deposited his books in the hall closet before doing chores.* 243

desperate (des ′ pər ət) – causing despair or in a despairing way; in an extreme way. *The drowning woman screamed desperately for help.* 250

desperation (des′ pər ā′ shən) – a feeling of hopelessness and despair. *In his desperation, Sandy could think of nothing left to try.* 102

devise (di vīz′) – to think up or plan. *Mom is trying to devise a way to surprise Dad on his birthday.* 204

dignity (dig′ nə tē) – quality of being stately, proper, and well-behaved. *The buck walked with silent dignity through the woods.* 136

disgruntled (dis grən′ təld) – discontented; upset or unhappy. *He is disgruntled because he could not have his own way.* 254

disheveled (di shev′ əld) – out of regular arrangement; disordered. *After his wild run through the brush, Eric's hair was disheveled and his face scratched.* 236

divert (dī vərt′) – to turn aside. *While Mary diverted Mom's attention, Nelson sneaked into the kitchen with a big bouquet of daisies.* 176

ebb (eb) – to recede or become less. *The fishermen left early with the ebbing of the tide.* 33

eliminate (i lim′ ə nāt) – get rid of; leave out or take out. *One way to find a correct answer is to eliminate all of the incorrect ones.* 250

emerge (i mərj′) – to appear. *The blankets heaved, and Paul's tousled head gradually emerged.* 184

emigrate (em′ i grāt) – to leave one's country or home to move somewhere else. *In the 1600s and 1700s, many Europeans emigrated to America where they could have religious freedom.* 146

engross (in grōs′) – take up the whole attention of. *Sheila was engrossed in a book and didn't hear her mother call.* 237

entrance (in trants′) – to fill with delight and fascination. *Julie was entranced by the dancing streamers of the aurora.* 42

exaggerate (ig zaj′ ər āt) – to make something seem larger or greater than it is. *Tom exaggerated when he said the new principal was 8 feet tall.* 226

expose (ek′ spōz) – to uncover; bring out into plain sight. *In three years of careful digging, the archaeologists had exposed an ancient temple.* 219

fascinate (fas′ i nāt) – to hold the interest of; to entrance. *The bright pictures in the book fascinated the baby.* 113

flail (flāl) – to swing or strike. *With his arms flailing wildly, the man tried to keep his balance on the rolling log.* 3

fleece (flēs) – the wool coat of a sheep or other animal. *That heavy fleece will make a warm, thick rug.* 52

foreigner (fór′ ən ər) – a person from another country. *The Bible says Christians are foreigners in the earth.* 14

forge (fórj) – a furnace or shop where iron is heated and shaped, as a blacksmith's shop. *Andy often stopped by the forge on his way home from school to watch Mr. Ellis at his work.* 118

game (gām) – willing. *Joy had never played Spoons, but when we offered to teach her, she was game to try.* 175

generous (jen′ ər əs) – unselfish; willing to give. *A generous person is more pleasant to be with than a selfish person.* 78

grimace (grim′ əs) – a twisting of the muscles of the face; a facial expression showing disapproval or pain. *Alice grimaced when the doctor touched her sprained ankle.* 227

Pronunciation Key: /ə/ but; /ä/ top; /yü/ use; /ər/ mother; /th/ thick; /<u>th</u>/ this; /ór/ corn; /ü/ boot; /u̇/ foot; /ó/ lost; /ói/ coin, toy; /är/ star; /au̇/ out; /zh/ measure; /ī r/ deer; /ĕr/ bear

grist (grist) – a batch of grain ready to be ground into meal or flour. *Every Monday, the farmers bring their grist to Thompson's Mill.* 176

grizzled (griz′ əld) – streaked with gray; grayish. *The old man had white hair and a grizzled beard.* 94

hempen (hem′ pən) – made of hemp. Hemp plant fibers can be twisted to make cord or rope. *Stout hempen rope is a handy thing to have.* 71

hostile (häs′ təl) – of or like an enemy; unfriendly. *When MaryJo told what Alan had done, he gave her a hostile look.* 110

humiliated (hyü mil′ ē āt′ əd) – embarrassed; ashamed. *Joe was humiliated when the teacher punished him for cheating.* 73

illegible (il′ lej′ ə bəl) – hard or impossible to read. *You will need to rewrite this, Tom—your writing is illegible.* 260

immigrant (im′ ə grənt) – a person who comes to settle in a new country. *My grandparents were Swedish immigrants.* 147

imperil (im per′ əl) – to put in danger. *Many times Paul imperiled his life for the Gospel.* 66

incite (in sīt′) – to stir up; to urge to action. *The man was arrested for inciting the riot.* 65

interpretation (in tər′ prə tā′ shən) – explanation; meaning. *Joseph told Pharaoh the interpretation of his dream.* 54

interview (in′ tər vyü′) – a meeting to answer questions or talk about something. *The boss held an interview with each applicant for the job.* 79

intuition (in′ tü wi′ shən) – a strong feeling; a hunch; knowing or sensing something without being told. *Many people think women have more intuition than men.* 103

jeopardize (jep′ ər dīz) – to risk; to put into danger. *I don't want to jeopardize my chances of getting an A by not studying.* 259

jostle (jäs′ əl) – to shove or push. *The big man jostled his way to the front of the crowd.* 99

justice (jəs′ təs) – being just or fair. *The laws of the United States try to give justice to everyone.* 72

launch (lȯnch) – to start off; to set a ship or boat afloat and start it on its journey. *Grandpa launched into a tale of his boyhood.* 147

lithe (līth) – quick and graceful. *The tall Indian walked with lithe, silent steps.* 43

loiter (loi′ tər) – to dawdle or linger. *The boys loitered on the way to school until they realized the time.* 44

luxurious (ləg zhər′ ē əs) – fine, rich, and comfortable. *"No," said Daddy, "we can't afford to stay at such a luxurious hotel."* 147

massacre (mas′ ə kər) – the killing of a large number of people. *News of the Indian massacre made the pioneers afraid.* 65

mechanically (mi kan′ i klē) – automatically; as if by machine. *Mechanically Nancy went through the motions of washing dishes, but her mind was far away.* 137

meddle (med′ əl) – to interfere with something that is not your business. *I've told you not to meddle with my model airplane.* 78

mesa (mā′ sə) – a hill with steep sides and a flat high top. *There are many mesas and buttes in the western United States.* 200

miniature (min′ ə chər) – something small of its kind. *Miniature goats are cute.* 185

miser (mī′ zər) – a greedy person who loves to get money. *A miser cannot go to heaven because he loves riches more than he loves God.* 74

moderate (mäd′ ər āt) – to become less strong. *After several hours, the wind moderated and I went to sleep.* 17

obscure (əb skyùr′) – to make something hard to see. *Fog swirled around us, obscuring the view and making it difficult for Dad to drive.* 30

ominous (äm′ ə nəs) – threatening. *The ominous darkness made us fear a bad storm.* 2

optimistic (äp′ tə mis′ tik) – cheerful and hopeful; trying to find something good in everything. *In spite of the weatherman's prediction of rain, Mina remained optimistic.* 135

panic (pan′ ik) – sudden, uncontrolled fear; to feel such fear. *Laurie panicked when the lights went out.* 8

partition (pär ti′ shən) – a wall or other divider that separates a room or building into smaller parts. *Thin partitions divided the church basement into Sunday school rooms.* 169

perplex (pər pleks′) – to puzzle or bewilder. *Marlin was perplexed when Alex would not speak to him.* 157

Pronunciation Key: /ə/ but; /ä/ top; /yü/ use; /ər/ mother; /th/ thick; /<u>th</u>/ this; /ȯr/ corn; /ü/ boot; /ù/ foot; /ȯ/ lost; /oi/ coin, toy; /är/ star; /aù/ out; /zh/ measure; /ir/ deer; /er/ bear

ply (plī) – to use diligently. *The canoeist plied his paddle well.* 4

ponderous (pän′ dər əs) – slow and clumsy because of being large. *The alligator made her ponderous trek from the river to her nest.* 184

predict (prē dikt′) – to tell what one thinks or expects to happen. *"Well, you'll do all right, but I'll probably get a bad grade," predicted Rod.* 115

prejudice (prej′ ə dəs) – an opinion formed without knowing the facts; disliking someone just because they are different. *Prejudice is wrong because it is not based on fact.* 86

principle (prin′ si pəl) – a rule to go by for right living. *In the Sermon on the Mount, Jesus gave us many principles for living the Christian life.* 80

query (kwir′ ē) – to ask or question. *"What do you think is the best thing to do?" queried Mary.* 66

reduction (rē dək′ shən) – being reduced; the act of reducing. *The city officials urged everyone to use buses and subways to help with traffic reduction.* 9

rejoinder (rē join′ dər) – an answer, especially a reply to a reply. *"I'm ready now," answered Regina. "Well, come on then," was Karen's curt rejoinder.* 157

reluctant (rē lək′ tənt) – unwilling; hesitating to do something. *Johnny had such a good time that he was reluctant to leave.* 58

resent (rē zent′) – to feel anger toward. *Josh resented Sue's questions about his plans for the evening.* 102

resolution (rez′ ə lü′ shən) – a firm decision. *I made a resolution to do my homework right away.* 200

resourceful (ri sȯrs′ fəl) – skillful at finding ways of doing things. *Mom is a resourceful housewife.* 137

respite (res′ pət) – a time of rest. *The men were glad for a respite from working in the hot sun.* 33

respond (ri spänd′) – 1. to answer or reply. *"Yes, I think I can make it," Ellen responded.* 2. to react in a good way. *Janice's infection is responding to the antibiotic the doctor prescribed.* 117

retort (ri tȯrt′) – to answer sharply. *Don't blame me—it's your own fault!" retorted Andy angrily.* 226

retrieve (ri trēv′) – to get back or recover something; to find and bring back. *Todd trained his dog to retrieve sticks.* 160

rival (rī′ vəl) – one of two or more people who are all trying to get something only one of them can have. *George W. Bush and Al Gore were rivals for the presidency in the 2000 election.* 147

rivet (riv′ ət) – to fasten. *Fear held him riveted to the spot.* 9

rueful (rü′ fəl) – mournful or regretful; pitiable; in a sorrowful way. *"I thought I knew what I was doing," said Johnny ruefully.* 251

runt (rənt) – something that is much smaller than others of its kind. *That puppy is the runt of the litter.* 85

salvage (sal′ vij) – to rescue or save from ruin or destruction. *Do you mean that that pretty sofa is salvaged from the junkyard?* 267

scrutinize (skrüt′ ən īze) – to examine closely. *Wayne bent to scrutinize the deer tracks on the trail.* 158

sever (sev′ ər) – to cut; to separate. *Dad severed the chicken's head from its body with one chop of the hatchet.* 185

sheepish (shē′ pish) – embarrassed or shy in an awkward way. *The little boy grinned sheepishly when his mother introduced him to us.* 227

shrewd (shrüd) – clever. *The Pharisees tried to confuse Jesus by asking Him shrewd questions.* 42

shudder (shəd′ ər) – to tremble, especially with fear. *Anna shuddered at what could have happened if she had not seen Timmy heading for the road.* 20

site (sīt) – a specific location. *There is a memorial at the site of the massacre.* 183

smite (smīt) – to hit or strike; to defeat. *God helped Gideon's army smite the Midianites.* 52

somber (säm′ bər) – dark and gloomy; dark colored. *The woman was dressed in somber gray.* 191

specify (spes′ ə fī) – to name; to state in detail. *They have not specified a date for the wedding.* 58

stark (stärk) – harsh and bare. *The twisted tree was a stark silhouette against the darkening sky.* 134

stressful (stres′ fəl) – causing strain or pressure. *It is always stressful when a family member dies.* 266

Pronunciation Key: /ə/ but; /ä/ top; /yü/ use; /ər/ mother; /th/ thick; /<u>th</u>/ this; /ȯr/ corn; /ü/ boot; /u̇/ foot; /ȯ/ lost; /ȯi/ coin, toy; /är/ star; /au̇/ out; /zh/ measure; /ïr/ deer; /ēr/ bear

structure (strək′ shər) – something that is built. *The bell tower was a tall structure in the town square.* 70

suspect (sə spekt′) – to guess. *I suspect Aaron is up to something, by that mischievous look on his face.* 59

teeter (tē′ tər) – to move unsteadily. *The girl teetered into the room on her high-heeled shoes.* 191

tempestuous (tem pes′ chə wəs) – stormy, troubled. *The sailors threw Jonah overboard into the tempestuous sea.* 124

territory (ter′ ə tȯr ē) – Any large area of land. *The United States bought the Louisiana Territory from France in 1803.* 110

tether (te′ t͟hər) – a rope or chain used to tie an animal; to tie an animal with a rope or chain. *Jerry tethered the goat to a post in the field.* 3

thoroughly (thər′ ō lē) – completely. *I thoroughly enjoyed the book I got for my birthday.* 99

traitorous (trā′ tər əs) – false, disloyal; like a traitor. *A traitorous little breeze blew sparks from the fire far across the prairie.* 5

transplant (trɑnts′ plɑnt′) – to move something, usually but not always a plant, from one location to another. *Mom transplanted her irises yesterday.* 85

unnerved (ən nərvd′) – nervous; upset. *Unnerved by the sounds in the dark jungle and the tales of the witch doctor, Wembo could hardly go on.* 67

upbraid (əp brād′) – to criticize or scold. *The policeman upbraided Dale for his reckless driving.* 65

vague (vāg) – not clear; indistinct. *Feeling a vague sense of danger, the man paused and looked behind him.* 44

vaunt (vȯnt) – to brag or show off one's own abilities. *God is not pleased when we vaunt our skills before other people.* 53

venomous (ven′ ə məs) – poisonous. *The copperhead is a venomous snake.* 128

verify (ver′ i fī) – to prove that something is true; to check the truth of something. *Can you verify the story?* 157

victuals (vit′ əlz) – food. *Bring your families, your friends, and some victuals, and we'll have a fine time.* 54

violence (vī′ə lənts) – using force to hurt someone. *The missionaries feared that the witch doctor might stir up the people to violence.* 111

whinny (whin′ ē) – to neigh. *Old Dobbin whinnied contentedly from his stall.* 2

wrench (rench) – 1. to cause to feel sorrow, as a twist inside. *The father's heart wrenched as he told his son about Grandpa's death.* 2. to snatch away with a violent twist. *Shari wrenched the keys from her brother's hand.* 86

zest (zest) – an exciting or interesting quality; relish, eagerness. *Justin is a lively person with a zest for life.* 176

Pronunciation Key: /ə/ but; /ä/ top; /yü/ use; /ər/ mother; /th/ thick; /<u>th</u>/ this; /ȯr/ corn; /ü/ boot; /u̇/ foot; /ȯ/ lost; /ȯi/ coin, toy; /är/ star; /au̇/ out; /zh/ measure; /ir/ deer; /er/ bear

Acknowledgements

Artist: Michelle Beidler and others

Cover artist and design: Michelle Beidler and David Miller

Editorial committee: Sterling Beachy, Jennifer Crider, Keith E. Crider, James Hershberger, Ava Shank

"as my eyes," a Chippewa song.

"Be Strong," by Maltbie D. Babcock.

"Boomerang" adapted from "They Thought it was Thomas," by Elmo Stoll. ©1968 Pathway Publishers, Aylmer, Ontario, Canada. All rights reserved. Used by permission.

"Brothers in Danger," adapted from "The White Brother," from *Lion Boy*, by Alden G. Stevens. ©1938 by Frederick A. Stokes Company.

"Chinook," by Eleanor Chance Long.

"Cold Winter," from *Away Goes Sally,* by Elizabeth Coatsworth.

"Dare to be True," by George Herbert.

"Down on the Shore," Author unknown.

"Emergency!" adapted from "Keeper of the Light." Adaptation ©2002 Christian Light Publications, Inc., Harrisonburg, VA. All rights reserved.

"Enemy in the Wilderness," adapted from "A Fire in the Wilderness" by Erick Berry from *Hearthstone in the Wilderness.* ©1944 The Macmillan Company.

"George Makes a Way," by Ruth K. Hobbs. ©2002 Christian Light Publications, Inc., Harrisonburg, VA. All rights reserved.

"Home on His Own," adapted from "Bishop Benedict," from *Walking With Jesus,* by Mary Clemens Meyer. Taken from a collection of stories put together by descendants of Benedict Miller. ©1992 Herald Press, Scottdale, PA. All rights reserved. Used by permission.

"I Remember, I Remember," by Thomas Hood.

"I Still Think it Was a Miracle," by Ruth K. Hobbs. ©1985 Ruth K. Hobbs, Harrisonburg, VA. All rights reserved. Used by permission.

"I Will Not Do It," from the King James Version Bible.

"In or Out," adapted from "The Latchstring." Adaptation ©2002 Christian Light Publications, Inc., Harrisonburg, VA. All rights reserved.

"In Spite of War," from *War-Torn Valley* by Joyce Miller. ©1990 Rod and Staff Publishers, Inc., Crockett, KY. All rights reserved. Used by permission.

"In the Carpenter Shop," Author unknown.

"Indian Boy," by Johnny Sloan. Reproduced with permission. *The Christian Science Monitor* (www.csmonitor.com). All rights reserved.

"Indian Names," by Lydia Huntly Sigourney, abridged.

"Invention From a Warm Heart," adapted from "Benjamin Franklin's Iron Stove," by Carolyn S. Bailey. Adaptation ©2002 Christian Light Publications, Inc., Harrisonburg, VA. All rights reserved.

"Jelly Beans Forever," by Ruth K. Hobbs. Adaptation ©2002 Christian Light Publications, Inc., Harrisonburg, VA. All rights reserved.

"Just the Same Inside," adapted from "The Desirable Shawl: A Story for Mother's Day," by Grace Purdie Moon, from *Chi-weé: The Adventures of a Little Indian Girl.* ©1925, 1952 by Caryl Moon Corey and Francis M. Moon. All rights reserved.

"Lions in the Night," adapted from "Watch the Camera, Mr. Lion," by Dick Douglas. Adaptation ©2002 Christian Light Publications, Inc., Harrisonburg, VA. All rights reserved.

"Love Your Enemies," from the King James Version Bible.

"My Home," by Elizabeth Hutto.

"Never Turned a Mill," adapted from "The Old Miller." Adaptation ©2002 Christian Light Publications, Inc., Harrisonburg, VA. All rights reserved.

"Of Giving," by Arthur Guiterman.

"Open Range," by Kathryn and Byron Jackson.

"Out to Old Aunt Mary's" by James Whitcomb Riley.

"Primer Lesson," by Carl Sandburg.

"Results and Roses," by Edgar Guest.

"School Bell," reprinted by permission of Harold Ober Associates Incorporated. Copyright ©1938 by Eleanor Farjeon. Copyright renewed 1966 by Gervase Farjeon.

"Ship Unsinkable," by Ruth K. Hobbs. ©2002 Christian Light Publications, Inc., Harrisonburg, VA. All rights reserved.

"Shipwreck!" from the King James Version Bible.

"Sleep-Out Below Zero," adapted from "The Little Postboy," by Bayard Taylor. Adaptation ©2002 Christian Light Publications, Inc., Harrisonburg, VA. All rights reserved.

"Some People I Know," copyright ©1983 by Jack Prelutsky from *The Random House Book of Poetry for Children* by Jack Prelutsky. Used by permission of Random House Children's Books, a division of Random House, Inc.

"Take it From Me—I Know," by Ruth K. Hobbs. Adaptation ©2002 Christian Light Publications, Harrisonburg, VA. All rights reserved.

"Test Room," adapted from "Do Not Meddle." Adaptation ©2002 Christian Light Publications, Inc., Harrisonburg, VA. All rights reserved.

"The Army That Was Too Big," from the King James Version Bible.

"The Bell of Atri," retold by James Baldwin.

"The Brook," by Alfred, Lord Tennyson.

"The Kayak," Author unknown.

"The Sandhill Crane," from *The Children Sing in the Far West* by Mary Austin. Copyright 1928 by Mary Austin, © renewed 1956 by Kenneth M. Chapman and Mary C. Wheelwright. Reprinted by permission of Houghton Mifflin Company. All rights reserved.

"The Shell," by Elizabeth Loeks Bouman.

"The Snow," adapted from "The Snow," Author unknown. Adaptation ©2002 Christian Light Publications, Inc., Harrisonburg, VA. All rights reserved.

"The Song My Paddle Sings," by Pauline Johnson.

"The Spring," by Rose Fyleman.

"The Water Ouzel Outwits an Enemy," from *All on a Mountain Day* by Aileen Fisher. Copyright ©1956 by Aileen Fisher. All rights renewed and reserved. Used by permission of Marian Reiner for the author.

"Till I Have Proof," adapted from "Michel and His Uncle Ives of Brittany," by Anna Milo Upjohn. Illustrations from "Michel and His Uncle Ives of Brittany," used by permission of DC Heath and Company.

"To Prove A Proverb," adapted from "The Water Barrel." Adaptation ©2002 Christian Light Publications, Inc., Harrisonburg, Virginia. All rights reserved.

"Underwater Fisherman," adapted from "A Fish for Your Bathtub—Sponge Fishing," by Don Henshaw.

"Wind and I," by Jennifer K. Crider. ©2002 Jennifer Crider, Front Royal, Virginia. All rights reserved. Used by permission.

"Words," by Robert Louis Stevenson.

"Zambezi Crisis," adapted from "The Word of a Gentleman," from *The Children's Story Caravan.*

Attempt has been made to secure permission for the use of all copyrighted material. If further information is received, the publisher will be glad to properly credit the material in future printings.